Salvaged from the *Mary Rose* in 1981: 16-sided bronze barrel, cast by F. Arcanus, 1535.

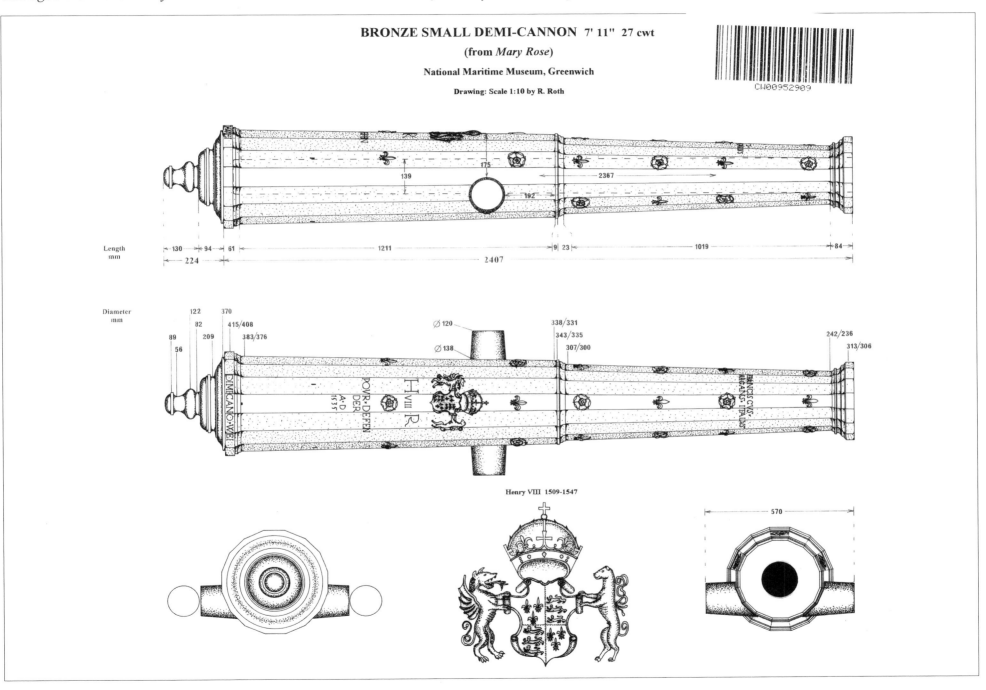

BRONZE SMALL DEMI-CANNON 7' 11" 27 cwt

(from *Mary Rose*)

National Maritime Museum, Greenwich

Drawing: Scale 1:10 by R. Roth

CW00952909

Length
mm

130 94 61 1211 9 23 1019 84
224 2407

139 175 2367 192

Diameter
mm

122 370
82 415/408
209 383/376
89
56

Ø 120
Ø 138

338/331
343/335
307/300

242/236
313/306

DIMICANO·WE   POVR·DEFEN DER   H VIII R   A·D 1535   FRANCIS CVS· ARCANS· ITPA LVS

Henry VIII 1509-1547

570

Naval Guns

NAVAL GUNS
500 Years of Ship and Coastal Artillery

Hans Mehl

Drawings by Rudolf Roth

CHATHAM PUBLISHING

LONDON

Picture sources

Author 212; Bath Iron Works 1; H. Beyer 2; Breda 1; S. Breyer collection 1; Blohm & Voss 1; M. Egger 10; F. Elchlepp 1; D. Flohr 1; A. Fraccaroli 1; Gröner archive 1; P. Hammer 1; G. Hein 1; Imperial War Museum 1; U. Israel 4; Jacob 1; H. Kanetzki 1; Trondenes Cannon Museum 1; H. Krummel 2; H.J. Mehl 5; K.P. Mehl 16; M. Meyer 18; Museo Tecnico Navale 4; B. Oesterle 4; O. Pestow 3; R. Pichulek 2; H.G. Prager 1; O. Rahardt 2; St. Rahardt 3; R. Roth 11; W. Schäfer 1; P. Tamm archive 14; Tessmer 1; D. Trapp 8; K. Trepping 2; US Navy 1; P. Vicary 1; Vientipaino Oy 1; Zentralbild 1; H. Kanetzki 1.

Copyright © Verlag E S Mittler & Sohn GmbH, Hamburg, 2001
English translation copyright © Chatham Publishing 2002

First published in Great Britain in 2002 by
Chatham Publishing, 99 High Street, Rochester
Kent ME1 1LX

Distributed by Gerald Duckworth & Co Ltd,
61 Frith Street, London W1D 3JL

First published in Germany in 2001 under the title
Schiffs- und Küstenartillerie Marinegeschütze aus 500 Jahren by
Verlag E S Mittler & Sohn GmbH, Hamburg, Germany

British Library Cataloguing in Publication Data
A catalogue record for this book is available from the
British Library

ISBN 1 86176 201 1

Translation by Keith Thomas

Typeset by E-Type, Liverpool

Printed in China by Compass Press Ltd

Contents

Foreword

Ships first began to carry gunpowder artillery in the mid-14th century, marking a significant milestone in the development of the warship. In ancient times various forms of mechanical artillery had been employed to hurl rocks, heavy bolts and incendiary projectiles at enemy ships, but the first true guns brought a significant improvement in accuracy. Naval guns, and the tactics for their use, developed continuously over the succeeding centuries, becoming an important factor in the exercise of sea power by maritime nations. Indeed, artillery both on land and sea has played just as important a part in world history as many other ground-breaking inventions.

Generally speaking, early naval artillery was primarily an anti-personnel weapon, although it could also hamper an enemy ship's manoeuvrability by damaging its rigging or rudder. For nearly 300 years naval battles were largely decided by boarding and hand-to-hand combat: it was only much later, with the development of more powerful guns and ship-of-the-line tactics that 'floating fortresses' mounting as many as 100 guns that warships were able to force their opponent's surrender by gunfire alone, although ships were only rarely actually sunk unless they caught fire and their magazines exploded. By this time, guns could wreak havoc on a ship's gun decks, inflicting hundreds of casualties, and even the victorious ship was likely to suffer severe damage and heavy losses.

In this book, the author provides the reader with a wealth of technical detail on a vast range of ships' guns and coastal artillery. This well-organised study represents a great deal of work and is a useful addition to the relatively small number of books on this subject.

Until carrier aviation reached its full maturity (eg at the Battle of Midway) and the later development of guided missiles, the naval gun was the most important weapon in the struggle for naval supremacy. Even in the 21st century, naval guns still have a role to play, in the form of rapid-fire automatic weapons with sophisticated fire control systems, and examples of these are also found in this book.

It only remains for me to recommend this comprehensive pictorial survey of naval artillery in the past 500 years as a major contribution to the subject, of particular relevance to modelmakers and collectors.

Peter Tamm

Introduction and Acknowledgements

If you are a historian, an enthusiast interested in naval history and the technical side of military matters, or a modelmaker specialising in the history of naval shipbuilding and ships' artillery, you may well be familiar with a number of the publications listed in the bibliography. These works, written by unchallenged experts such as Peter Padfield, Jean Boudriot, John Campbell and Paul Schmalenbach, together with a range of other publications concerned with specialised aspects of the history of naval artillery, provide an excellent starting point even for newcomers to this field. As might be expected, most of these publications feature a wide range of illustrations, but nevertheless it is the comprehensive text which tend to dominate, with the photographs and drawings illustrating particular points or weapons. This is precisely the reason for the present volume, which is designed to complement these books by providing a wealth of pictorial material, accompanied by brief accounts of the development of the various gun types, together with selected technical and ballistic data. This book does not claim to be comprehensive in its coverage of the history of naval artillery, but the collection of pictures of guns and models – the fruit of over 30 years' work – does give a representative insight into the history of ship and coastal artillery in the past 500 years. The overwhelming majority of the photographs show guns which survive today in museums or on preserved ships, but even here it would be quite impossible to illustrate all the weapons that have ever been built and installed. Heavy artillery and gun turrets represent valuable scrap metal, and most were sacrificed to the cutting torch once their ships were decommissioned. A considerable proportion of warships of all classes, complete with their weapons, today lie at the bottom of all the world's oceans. It was my intention to bridge the many gaps between the surviving guns, and to this end the book also includes weapons which are to be

found to this day at war memorials all over the world, at patriotic sites (USA), in national and private collections, and also at heritage sites, in addition to collections of guns and special displays in museums. For just a few important guns I have been obliged to use pictures from dockyard and official archives. Many of these weapons have had a vital role to play in history, and give an insight into trends in development, special-purpose applications and, in some cases, technical details and special design features relating to their manufacture and use. Where the book includes guns

A Dutch 6pdr Drake, cast by Assuerus Koster for the East India Company; it is a fine example of the elegant ornamentation on some bronze barrels. (Ramsgate Maritime Museum, Great Britain)

which are on display at memorials, and also in the case of those few weapons salvaged from the bottom of the sea, I trust that due respect will be shown towards those who fell in many naval wars and sea battles.

Few early guns have survived complete with their mountings, and those gun barrels which have (such as those from the Vasa) are of particular importance, even when the carriage is incomplete. There can be no doubt of the skill of those early gunfounders and their workers; ample evidence is provided especially by the bronze barrels of all calibres with their rich ornamentation featuring beautiful coats of arms and insignia, often designed by famous engravers, artists or architects. I have been able to include superb drawings of a few of these valuable pieces thanks to the friendly support of

the Swiss artillery expert, Rudolf Roth.

The methods of manufacturing these guns, and the technological requirements of these techniques, are described in some of the publications listed in the bibliography, starting with wrought iron pieces and ringed stave-built barrels, progressing through cast iron and bronze muzzle-loaders, and concluding with rifled breech-loaders. If you wish learn about these technologies, especially the methods of production of bronze cannon and mortars, I most warmly recommend the book *The Art of Gunfounding* by Carel de Beer. This volume includes fifty unique colour drawings by Jan Verbruggen illustrating the complete manufacturing process for bronze barrels, reproduced in large format (Jan and Pieter Verbruggen were Dutch gunfounders who were employed by the British from 1770).

The development of modern guns, including automatic weapons, always went hand-in-hand with advances in other areas of science, most importantly metallurgy and material sciences, mechanical engineering and – not least – pyrotechnics. The constant widening of knowledge concerning internal and external ballistics provided the basis for continual improvements in accuracy and range. The contest between calibre, penetrative power and armour protection has been widely documented. Without doubt a genuine revolution in military thinking came about with the development and introduction of modern radar fire control systems, making it possible to fire the heaviest shells accurately at extreme range without the use of optical gunsights. The same technology was subsequently applied to anti-aircraft artillery. These innovations were followed, as we all know, by high-speed computer systems which have today completely automated such processes as target location and tracking. Today, it is almost possible for a gunnery officer to concentrate on drinking his coffee while his guns automatically attack the target. (Provided, that is, that his systems work!) Rates of fire are now extremely high, and Maxim and Nordenfelt would never have dared to dream of 4000 or more rounds per minute, now possible with calibres up to 30mm. To round off this excursion into modern weapons systems the book also briefly describes a few present-day guns.

The descriptions of the guns have been kept in chronological order and divided up as far as possible according to calibre. The names given for the weapons are those known to have been used at the time, or commonly used in the country of their origin, in so far as this information is known. In the text accompanying the photographs, the reader will find basic information in metric units relating to calibre, dimensions and weight. The appendix lists a selection of historically important and/or foreign units of measurement, intended to help the reader make his own conversions when carrying out further research. As other authors have already made abundantly clear, data such as the length or diameter of a gun barrel is often uncertain. In any case it is seldom stated where and at what point these dimensions apply. As far as possible, the information given in this book relating to smooth-bore guns, and also to some rifled muzzle-loaders and breech-loaders, is based on my own measurement of the barrels and/or measurements taken by Rudolf Roth. Dimensions of

Off the tourist track: the remains of the Swedish Nya-Älfsborg coastal battery including cast iron 12pdrs manufactured by the Swedish iron foundry Stafsjö Bruk, cast around 1780.

more modern guns are taken either from manufacturers' specifications, service regulations or information from museums.

For several centuries ships' armament and coastal defence have been intimately connected, in that coastal artillery was designed to offer covering fire to a friendly fleet if it was forced to withdraw into port, engage enemy fleets offshore and prevent landings. Initially set up in simple field emplacements, such guns were subsequently mounted in coastal forts and bunkers; these developments are already well documented.

The coastal guns included in this volume alongside the ships' guns were – with a few exceptions – designed and built specifically for that purpose. However, in quite a number of cases actual naval guns were pressed into service on land after warships were decommissioned, and sometimes a weapon in service with the fleet was also used for coastal defence. We have evidence of this practice even with early muzzle-loaders, and later ships' guns were frequently installed in special mountings for coastal defence.

Although some ships' heavy guns ended their useful lives as coastal artillery, in this book these weapons feature in the ships' guns section. Decommissioned ships' guns were also installed on armoured trains or as railway guns, operated by naval crews. Furthermore, specially-built naval railway guns were employed in the USA and by the former Soviet Union for coastal defence and also on land fronts. Field guns were also employed increasingly for coastal defence, but this book does not cover these army weapons

The selection of outstanding barrel drawings by Rudolf Roth included in the book, together with a number of contemporary drawings and sketches of gun types, are intended to supplement the photographs, as well as to give the reader ideas for further study. It must be obvious that a pictorial description of period ships' guns and coastal artillery would no longer be possible single-handed, and I am greatly indebted to a number of directors of institutions and museums for their friendly assistance and support, and also to many individuals, good friends and acquaintances.

Pride of place here must go to the Hamburg publisher Peter Tamm, who is also the founder of the Wissenschaftliches Institut für Schiffahrts- und Marinegeschichte. He permitted me to photograph approximately thirty period naval guns from his own collection, and also gave me unrestricted access to his extensive library and comprehensive document archive. For permission to use pictures, provision of information

Not yet on display in museums: Russian AK-100 100mm L/59 guns on frigates of the 'Krivak II' class.

regarding specific gun types, permission to use technical data from publications and friendly exchanges of correspondence I wish to thank the Director of the Navy Museum in Washington D.C., Kim Nielsen; the Director of the ASSONAVE Institute in Rome, Vice-Admiral (retd.) Renato Sicurezza; the Director of the Orlogsmuseet in Copenhagen, Ole Lisberg Jensen; and the Director of Marine Archaeology at Kalmar Läns Museum, Lars Einarson. I also have to thank the directors of Conway Maritime Press Ltd, London, and the Director of the DAWA News Agency in Cologne, Harry Lippman, for their permission to use information from their sources.

A very special vote of thanks is due to the Swiss artillery expert, Rudolf Roth. He not only made his fantastic barrel drawings available to me, but also supplied extensive notes and information relating to the pictures of early muzzle-loading weapons. The same applies to Manfred Meyer of the Wissenschaftliches Institut für Schiffahrts- und Marinegeschichte of Hamburg, who provided me with pictorial material together with much useful information and source material relating to Scandinavia. I also wish to thank Dr Martin Egger from Switzerland, who provided pic-

Russian coastal guns on the Finnish fortified island of Suomenlinna. In the foreground: Obuchov 6in/35 gun, 1885, on a coastal mount (see also p69).

tures and information gathered from his visits to Manila and Brazil.

I wish also to extend my gratitude to the following individuals for information derived from their scientific work (underwater archaeology) and pictorial material they supplied from educational and research expeditions: Dipl. Mus. Thomas Förster and Dipl. Mus. Ronald Pichulek, Rear-Admiral (retd.) Dr Fritz Elchlepp, Captain (retd.) Peter Hammer, FKpt (retd.) Dietrich Trapp, FKpt (retd.) Ulrich Israel, FKpt (retd.) Dipl. Ing. Olaf Pestow, Lieutenant (retd.) Helmut Krummel and Messrs Bernd Oesterle, Joachim Jacob, Olaf and Steffen Rahardt. My thanks also to my sons, Hans-Joachim and Klaus Peter, for providing photos of rare guns in museums. The following individuals rendered valuable help in obtaining and providing source material: the Director of the Deutsche Gesellschaft für Schiffahrts- und Marinegeschichte, Dr Hartmut Klüver, and the librarian of the Wissenschaftliches Institut für Schiffahrts- und Marinegeschichte, Holger Sterzenbach.

If this pictorial history of naval guns adds to the knowledge of interested individuals, and succeeds in filling some gaps in the knowledge of a few experts, then all the work will have been worthwhile.

Hans Mehl

Kritzmow/Hamburg, May 2001

The 1880 class of recruits in a souvenir photo in front of the 28cm Krupp cannon in the Friedrichsort fort on the Kieler Förde (barrel weight marked on trunnion: 27,486kg).

I. SHIPS' GUNS

Wrought iron chamber pieces and cast muzzle-loaders up to 1850

14th-century 2pdr chamber piece

This 14th-century wrought iron chamber piece was salvaged from the sea bed off the Danish island of Anholt in 1942. The weapon, to which the general term culverine is also applied, is a breech-loader with separate powder chamber. The rings around the round wrought barrel are clearly visible; they were forged and shunk onto the barrel when hot. The barrel is supported in a simple wooden box bed or stock, to which it was secured by iron bands. After the powder chamber had been loaded it was placed at the rear end of the barrel, and secured with a wedge. The charge was ignited via

2pdr chamber piece. (Orlogsmuseet Copenhagen, Denmark)

a touch-hole in the powder chamber. Nothing is known about the ship on which this weapon was installed.

Find from the Haarlemmermeer

This wrought chamber piece – in this case without its reinforcing rings – belongs to the Nederlandsch Museum voor Geschiedenis en Kunst in Amsterdam. The manufacture of the weapon, which was salvaged from the bottom of the Haarlemmermeer, has been dated to the early 16th century. Clearly visible is the simple block mount, which was often used to secure the barrel of such weapons. The chamber placed in the charging well has a recessed flange which fits inside the barrel.

(Rijksmuseum, Amsterdam)

Dutch hailshot gun. (Koninklijk Nederlands Legeren Wapenmuseum Delft. Inv. No. KNLWM 013334)

European Peterara, *c*1600

This wrought-iron peterara, made in Southern Europe, features an early form of yoke attached to the swivel stock. This was used in conjunction with a pin and a series of holes to set the barrel at a fixed elevation, and would have made it much easier for a single gunner to reload the gun quickly. A separate powder chamber with handle for breech-loading can be seen at bottom right. The calibre of this weapon is 65mm, the length of the barrel 736mm, and the overall length 1368mm. It was obviously intended for use as a swivel gun. Nothing more is known about the exact origins of this weapon.

Dutch hailshot gun, *c*1480

This chamber piece, known as a hailshot gun, is typical of the armament of ships in the 15th and 16th centuries, which were produced in various sizes. The wrought-iron weapon, produced in a Flemish workshop, has a calibre of 84mm. As a breech-loader it would have had several powder chambers – not shown here – one of which was fitted into the barrel after the projectiles had been inserted. The tapered end of the chamber fitted into the barrel, and it was secured with a cross-wedge. The gun would usually have fired bags filled with musket balls, ancestors of the later 'case shot' or 'canister shot'. The central ring with trunnion and the handle show that it was used as a swivel gun. The length of the barrel alone is 463mm, the overall length 872mm. The barrel bears the letter 'W'. Drawings by a Dutch shipbuilder dating from 1470 prove that a Dutch carrack would have carried at least ten such weapons. Two very similar weapons were also found on the wreck of the Dutch ship *Mauritius*, sunk in 1609 off the coast of Ghana.

European Peterara. (Woolwich Rotunda Museum, Great Britain, Inv. No. 1-8)

16th-century Portuguese chamber piece

This wrought-iron chamber piece, also known in this calibre by the Spanish term Lombarda, was salvaged in 1962 from the wreck of a Portuguese East Indiaman off the coast of the island of Madagascar. As a breech-loader the internal diameter at the rear end of the barrel is enlarged to accept the shoulder of a powder chamber (not shown). The calibre of the barrel, which is severely corroded internally, is around 130mm, the length 900mm and the maximum outside diameter at the end of the barrel 220mm. Such barrels were generally mounted in timber-framed boxes, to which they were secured with iron bands. A stiffened cross-piece in the frame would have provided a means of wedging the powder chamber once inserted.

Portuguese chamber piece. (Peter Tamm collection, Hamburg, Germany)

Portuguese chamber piece. (Peter Tamm collection, Hamburg, Germany)

16th-century Portuguese chamber piece

This wrought-iron chamber piece was salvaged from the same wreck as the previous gun; its powder chamber is also missing. Although the gun has a smaller calibre, the barrel features two lifting eyes attached to the reinforcing bands, with rings attached. The calibre is *c*100mm, the barrel length 1260mm and the diameter at the rear end 175mm.

French 1pdr Pierrier. (Musée de la Marine, Paris, France)

Copper chamber piece, 1551

In 1985 navy divers off Mukran salvaged a section of a gun barrel from the remains of a shipwreck at the island of Ruegen, and this find is shown in the photograph. Subsequent research showed that it was the wreck of a Danish-Lübeck ship which had been set on fire and sunk in 1565 by a Swedish squadron during the Northern War of 1563-70. The section of barrel salvaged is 700mm long, and is part of a breech-loading chamber piece, cast using an alloy containing 95.5 per cent copper, 1.5 per cent zinc and 2.0 per cent lead. The measured calibre is 50mm. On the breech end of the barrel the ornamentation is very well preserved, and includes acanthus leaves and the coat of arms of the Danish King Christian III (1534-59). The long section of the barrel bears the inscription CHRISTIAN VON GOTES / GENAD KON / IG CH THO DE / NEMARCEN / NOR-WEGEN / UND DER GO /TEN ANNO DOMINI 1551 (Christian, by the grace of God King of Denmark, Norway and the Goths, year of our Lord 1551).

Two separate powder chambers were also salvaged, and were found to fit this barrel. They are 450mm long, with an external diameter of 220mm and an internal diameter of 40mm. The barrel and one powder chamber

French 1pdr Pierrier, *c*1700

This weapon, on display in the Musée de la Marine, Paris, features a swivel mounting by means of a yoke pivoting in a tripod bracket mount. The weapon is a breech-loader, and has a calibre of 50mm. The separate powder chamber with integral handle was engaged in the breech from the rear, and fixed in place with a flat wedge. The length of the barrel up to the chamber flange is 650mm. The length including breech is 900 mm (excluding handle).

The loose fit of the trunnions in the yoke eye leads us to conclude that this mount was originally intended for a different weapon.

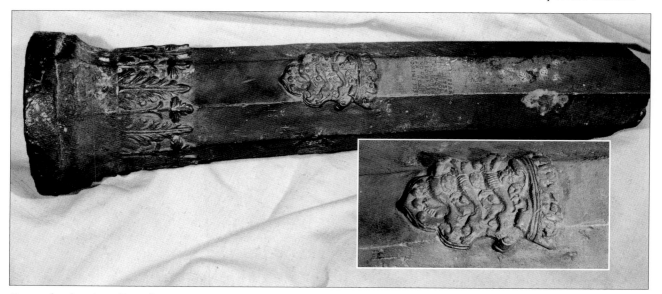

Copper chamber piece. (Rostock maritime museum, Germany)

are marked with the letter A (the other powder chamber, B). Comparisons of gun design and inscriptions led experts to surmise that the barrel was cast in the Freiburg area by the gunfounder Wolfgang Hilger (1511-77). The trunnions originally present indicate that this weapon was used as a swivel gun. To retain the powder chamber at the rear end of the barrel a strong chamber well must have been attached; the acanthus leaves are only present on the upper half of the barrel. However, it is also possible that the barrel was secured to a timber block mount, which would have been fitted with a strong cross-piece to accept a wedge for securing the powder chamber.

Spanish 6pdr Saker, 1551

This 6pdr saker was made for the Spanish crown, and was cast by Remigy de Halut in Flanders in 1551. The elegant bronze piece – here set up on a simplified display mount – was taken as a prize from a captured Dunkirk privateer off Enkhuizen in 1622. The calibre of the

Spanish 6pdr Saker. (Town Hall, Enkhuizen, Netherlands)

weapon is 93mm. The length of the barrel as far as the breech ring is 3207mm, plus 185mm for the cascabel, for an overall length of 3392mm. The weight of the barrel is 1104kg. The first reinforce of the gun bears the coat of arms of Emperor Charles V framed by the pillars of Hercules. It is evident just from looking at this 'long barrel gun' just how difficult it must have been for the gunners to reload such 6pdr guns on the ships of the Spanish Armada (1588).

Dutch 24pdr muzzle-loader, 1615

This bronze muzzle-loader is decorated at the breech end with the Dutch lion coat of arms, the year 1615 and, on the scroll below it, the word Zeelandia. The breech ring bears the inscription JOHANNIS BVRGER-HUYS ME FECIT MIDDELBVRG (Made by Johannis Burgerhuys, Middelburg), indicating the gunfounder and the place of manufacture. The cascabel itself takes the form of a flower rosette with a projecting pommel. The centre section features two well-preserved dolphin handles cast into the barrel. The inscription states that

Dutch 24pdr muzzle-loader. (Peter Tamm collection, Hamburg, Germany)

The bronze barrel of a Spanish 6pdr Saker, 1551.

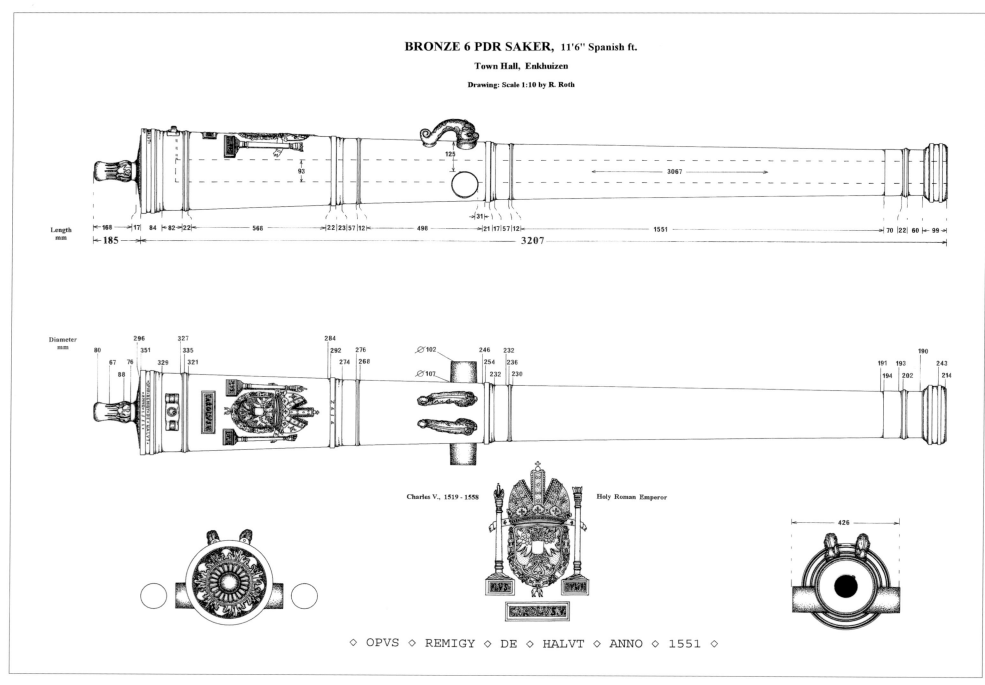

BRONZE 6 PDR SAKER, 11'6" Spanish ft.

Town Hall, Enkhuizen

Drawing: Scale 1:10 by R. Roth

Charles V., 1519 - 1558   Holy Roman Emperor

◇ OPVS ◇ REMIGY ◇ DE ◇ HALVT ◇ ANNO ◇ 1551 ◇

German-Spanish 6pdr muzzle-loader. (Kalmar Läns museum, Sweden, Inv. No. KLM 101 KR)

the barrel (the carriage is a reconstruction) is the property of the Dutch Admiralty of Zeeland.

The calibre is 14cm. The length of the barrel to the breech ring is 334cm, over the pommel 352cm. The maximum diameter at the rear is 43.6cm.

German-Spanish 6pdr muzzle-loader, *c*1620

This bronze barrel was salvaged from the wreck of the Swedish warship *Kronan* off the island of Oeland in 1981. The ship had sunk on 1 June 1676 during the Scanian War of 1675-79, soon after a powder charge exploded before the start of an action against a Danish-Dutch squadron under Admiral Cornelius Tromp. The armament of the *Kronan* consisted of 126 bronze cannon, of which half were German and Spanish pieces which had been captured during the Thirty Years War. Amongst them were some Spanish 12pdr and 6pdr guns, which had been delivered to Wismar for Wallenstein's fleet in 1628. The barrel shown here, mounted on a simplified carriage, was manufactured at a foundry in the Harz mountains for the Catholic League. The tulip-

shaped swelling of the muzzle shows that it was a ship's gun. The reinforce, which features cast-in dolphin handles, bears the coat of arms of King Philip IV of Spain.

Swedish 24pdr from the *Vasa*, 1626

This bronze muzzle-loader is one of forty-eight guns of the same calibre formerly carried by the Swedish warship *Vasa*. The ship capsized during her first voyage and sank at Tegelviken on 10 August 1628. The barrel shown here is mounted in a restored original carriage, and was cast in 1626 at the gun foundry in Stockholm. The bronze alloy has a copper content of 92 per cent, and the calibre of the barrel is 14cm. The reinforce bears the Swedish Imperial coat of arms and the letters GARS for 'Gustavus Adolphus Rex Sueciae' (Gustavus Adolphus, King of Sweden). The wealth of ammunition salvaged from the wreck in 1961 shows these guns fired a wide range of projectiles, including solid shot, langridge, bar shot, and case shot.

Swedish 24pdr from the Vasa. *(Vasa museum, Stockholm, Sweden)*

Dutch 24pdr muzzle-loader. (Woolwich Rotunda museum, Great Britain, Inv. No. 2-171 B)

Dutch 24pdr muzzle-loader, 1630

This bronze muzzle-loader was made for the Zeeland Chamber of the Dutch East India Co., and was cast in 1630 by M Burgerhuys. The barrel is in an excellent state of preservation, and was salvaged from the wreck of an East Indiaman in Chinese waters. The picture clearly shows the elegant proportions of Burgerhuys' barrels. The calibre of the smooth-bore barrel is 154mm. The barrel is 3029mm long plus 263mm for the cascabel and pommel, and weighs 2227kg.

Danish 24pdr muzzle-loader, 1631

This bronze 24pdr muzzle-loader was cast by Felix Fuchs in 1631. The reinforce displays the insignia of the Danish king Christian IV. The vent of this barrel runs from the cascabel to the charge chamber. The carriage is a reconstruction, painstakingly built as a copy of surviving original parts, and with the help of Swedish historians. The barrel was salvaged by divers near Göteborg in 1961.

Danish 24pdr muzzle-loader (see also p65). (Orlogsmuseet Copenhagen, Denmark)

The 24pdr Burgerhuys barrel for the East India Company.

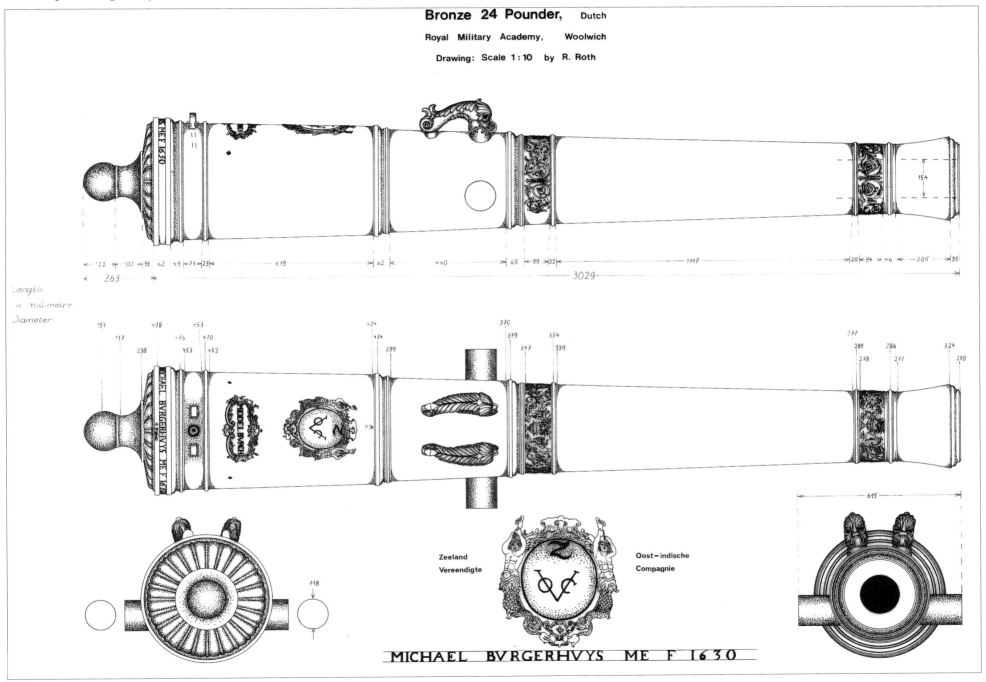

Bronze 24 Pounder, Dutch

Royal Military Academy, Woolwich

Drawing: Scale 1:10 by R. Roth

Length in millimetre

Diameter:

Zeeland Vereenigte — Oost–indische Compagnie

MICHAEL BVRGERHVYS ME F 1630

French 24pdr muzzle-loader. (St. Petersburg artillery museum, Russia)

British Iron 'Cannon of 7', 1673

This 7in gun was cast by John Brown in 1673, during the reign of Charles II. In 1695 this cast-iron muzzle-loader of the Rupertino type formed part of the armament of the British First Rate ship of the line HMS *Queen*, which had been launched in 1692. The outstanding feature of the barrels of these weapons is the unusually good quality of casting, produced by a special manufacturing process. However, the technique was expensive, and only a few hundred pieces were made. The calibre of this weapon is 183mm, which makes it equivalent to a 42pdr gun. The length of the barrel is 2928mm (overall length 3294mm) and it weighs about 3075kg (60-2-5).

French 24pdr muzzle-loader, 1636

This richly ornamented bronze barrel with two dolphin handles was cast in France in 1636, and in 1714 formed part of the armament of a Turkish warship. In the same year several of these guns were captured by the Russian fleet after a battle in the Black Sea. Later the barrel was set up on a fortress mounting. The calibre of the smooth-bore barrel is 152mm and it weighs 2204kg.

British iron 'Cannon of 7'. (Woolwich Rotunda Museum, Great Britain, Inv. No. 3 – 13)

The cast iron 'Rupertinoe' barrel of a 'Cannon of 7'.

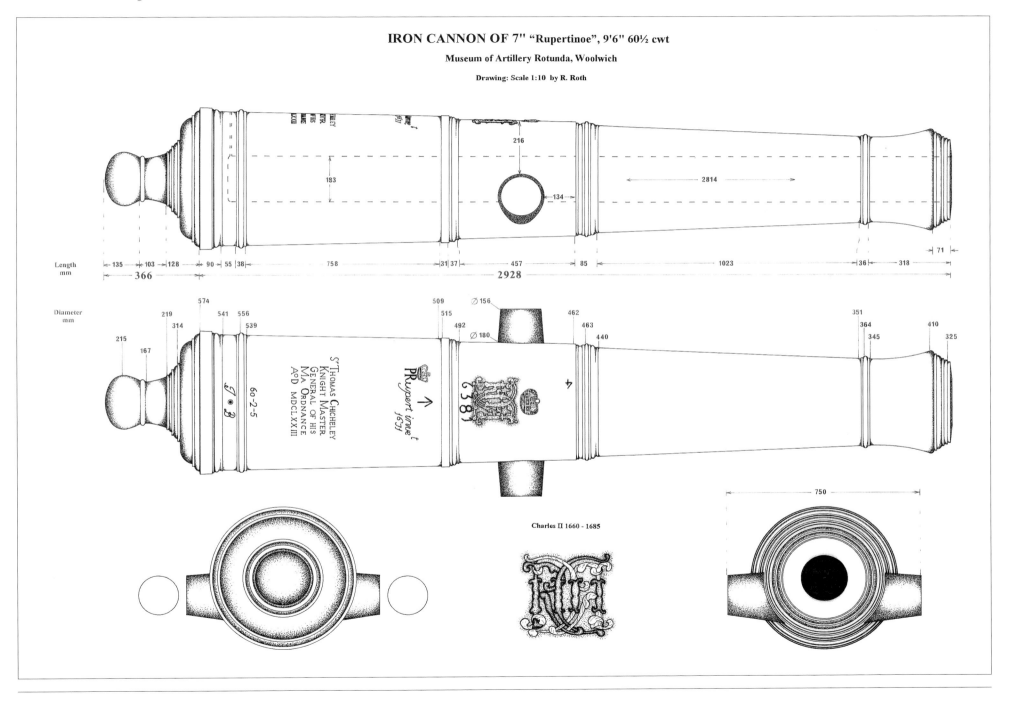

IRON CANNON OF 7" "Rupertinoe", 9'6" 60½ cwt

Museum of Artillery Rotunda, Woolwich

Drawing: Scale 1:10 by R. Roth

Charles II 1660 - 1685

This picture shows the 7in iron cannon during a test firing in Chatham Dockyard in 1992. The charge is only 70 per cent of normal (3.6kg gunpowder and 13.5kg sand), but it still gives an impression of a broadside from a ship of the line!

Swedish 24pdr muzzle-loader (see also p65). (Kalmar castle, Sweden)

Swedish 24pdr muzzle-loader, c1670

During the Scanian War, which has already been mentioned, a Danish squadron under Admiral Niels Juel attacked the Swedish fleet off Kalmar after the loss of his ship *Enigheden*. The Swedish ship *Nykeln* (launched 1664) had run aground, and was shot to pieces (the powder magazine exploded) by four Danish ships on 20 July 1678. The cast-iron 24pdr shown in this picture was salvaged from the latter ship in 1908/9. Its calibre is approximately 18cm, and it was subsequently set up on the ramparts of Kalmar castle. The reinforce bears the coat of arms of King Charles XI of Sweden (1660-97), but it is otherwise unadorned.

Danish 12pdr muzzle-loader. (Kalmar castle, Sweden)

Dutch 2pdr chamber piece (see also p67). (Peter Tamm collection, Hamburg, Germany)

Danish 12pdr muzzle-loader, *c*1675

Several period guns have been set up on the ramparts of Kalmar castle in Sweden, as a memorial to the conflict between Denmark and Sweden in the Scanian War. This 12.5cm calibre cast-iron muzzle-loader was part of the armament of the Danish warship *Enigheden*, which ran aground during an attack on a Swedish fleet in Kalmar Sound. On 2 July 1678 the Danish commander, Admiral Niels Juel, allowed the ship to sink, as it was taking on water. Guns and other equipment from the vessel were salvaged as early as 1908/9. Another gun from the *Enigheden* is currently on display in the Tojhusmuseet in Copenhagen.

Dutch 2pdr chamber piece, *c*1730

This bronze Crans pattern chamber piece represents a further development of the principle of employing quickly-changed powder chambers, as used on early breech-loaders, but in this case with a cast barrel. The barrel and charge well are cast in a single piece.

At both sides of the well rectangular openings can be seen through which a cross-wedge was forced in order to ram the chamber home. An additional cast lug prevented the chamber rotating. The charge was ignited by means of a vent in the chamber. The reinforce displays crossed anchors, the symbol of a Dutch Admiralty, presumably of Amsterdam.

The calibre of this weapon is 6.3cm. The barrel itself is 75.5cm long, the overall length including well 103cm. The diameter at the rear end of the barrel is 13.6cm. The external diameter of the powder chamber is 13.6cm, the internal diameter 3.3cm. This gives a wall thickness of 1.65cm. The powder chamber is 21.5cm long.

British heavy 24pdr muzzle-loader. (Tower of London, Great Britain, Inv. No. XIX – 48)

British heavy 24pdr muzzle-loader, 1743

This bronze muzzle-loader, cast by A. Schalch in 1743, formed part of the middle deck battery of the British First Rate three-decker ship of the line HMS *Royal George* (ex *Royal Anne*, launched 1756). The ship capsized in Portsmouth Harbour in 1782, but it proved possible to salvage the guns and some of the vessel's equipment. This barrel, cast originally for a siege gun, has a calibre of 150mm. It is a heavy pattern weapon, and the barrel weighs no less than 2603kg. The length to the breech ring is 2894mm, plus 261mm for cascabel and pommel, giving an overall length of 2603mm. The reinforce is adorned with the insignia of King George II (1727-60).

Spanish 24pdr muzzle-loader, 1746

The Musée de la Marine in Paris houses much of interest, including this richly ornamented bronze barrel belonging to a Spanish naval gun. The reinforce displays the coat of arms of King Ferdinand VI of Spain (1746-59). The band below the coat of arms bears the inscription FERDINANDVS VI. HISPANIARVM ET. INDIARVM ('Ferdinand VI, of Spain and the Indies'). The peripheral inscription around the breech ring reads JOSEPHUS. BAR (-) ULA. FECIT. BARNE, indicating that it was cast by a gunfounder of that name in Barne in the year 1746.

Spanish 24pdr muzzle-loader. (Musée de la Marine, Paris, France)

Prussian 3pdr battalion gun. (Peter Tamm collection, Hamburg, Germany)

British Armstrong pattern 4pdr muzzle-loader, 1750

On 11 June 1770 the naval barque *Endeavour* ran aground on the Barrier Reef, and this 4pdr muzzle-loader is one of the six guns which Captain James Cook ordered to be thrown overboard in order to lighten ship. The cast-iron barrel has a calibre of 83mm and a barrel length of 1820mm; the weight of the barrel is around 587.3kg. On the second reinforce we find the cypher of George II (1727-60). The *Endeavour* carried a total of ten guns, which were intended only to be used to defend the vessel against pirates, or from attack by natives. All six cannon thrown overboard were found again, but not until a special diving expedition was organised near Cape Tribulation in 1969.

Prussian 3pdr battalion gun, *c*1750

In November 1972 three British divers made a curious discovery in Plymouth Sound. At a depth of 13.5m they located the wreck of an unidentified British ship, and in it this cast bronze gun barrel. An interesting feature is the clearly visible bronze mount for a flintlock firing mechanism which had been added at a later date. The barrel, numbered 96, bears the insignia of the Prussian king Frederick II on the reinforce, with the scroll above it proclaiming ULTIMA RATIO REGIS ('The Last Argument of Kings'). The chase displays the Prussian coat of arms complete with eagle, together with the inscription PRO GLORIA & PATRIA ('For Glory and Homeland'). At the breech ring the cast charge is stated as NO 51 BR, and the weight of the barrel is also marked as 53 PF (533 Prussian pounds). The calibre is 7.5cm, the length of the barrel 147cm, and overall length 155cm. The measured diameter at the breech ring is 21cm. We can only guess how this barrel came into British hands. According to British historians the wreck could also be simply that of a fairly small ship or a private yacht.

British 4pdr Armstrong pattern muzzle-loader (see also p67).
(National Maritime Museum, Sydney, Australia)

Cyphers and Coats of Arms from British cast iron and bronze gun barrels.

Cyphers and Coat of Arms of British Monarchs

King George I reign 1714 - 1727

Iron Ordnance

Brass Ordnance

Brass Ordnance

King George III reign 1760 - 1820

Iron Ordnance

King George II reign 1727 - 1760

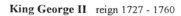

Iron Ordnance

Brass Ordnance

Brass Ordnance

Brass Ordnance

Brass Ordnance

M20© 1996, R. Roth

British 12pdr on the gunboat *Philadelphia*

The oared gunboat *Philadelphia* was built in 1776, and ranks as the oldest of all American warships. At the bow she was armed with a 12pdr cast-iron muzzle-loading cannon. A second gun, a Swedish 9pdr, was mounted amidships, and thus could provide broadside fire. Nearly all the guns on the first US warships had been captured from British transports or forts during the War of Independence. This gunboat (gondola) was sunk by a superior force of British ships on 11 October 1776 during the battles for Valcour Island on Lake Champlain. Re-discovered in 1935, she was raised that same year. She is in relatively good condition, and is now on display in the National Museum for American History.

British 12pdr on the gunboat Philadelphia *(National Museum for American History, Washington D.C., USA)*

(Museum frigate Jylland, Ebeltoft, Denmark)

Danish 30pdr bronze cannon, 1768

Denmark lost most of its seagoing fleet in 1807, and as a result suffered a shortage of purpose-built naval guns; the shortfall was made good by converting a number of older field guns or siege guns by installing them on naval carriages. Two of these guns were pressed into service to arm the steam frigate *Jylland* in 1862. The bronze barrels, cast in the Frederiksvaerk works as far back as 1768, during the reign of King Christian VII, are fitted with handles in the shape of elephants. The reinforce of one barrel shows the insignia of Christian VII (C7) and the second a portrait of the king. Both guns also saw action on 9 May 1864 in the battle between Danish and Austrian squadrons off Helgoland.

Danish 12pdr bronze cannon. (Orlogsmuseet Copenhagen, Denmark)

British Blomefield Pattern Iron 24pdr, 1786

The legendary HMS *Victory* (commissioned 1765) is on display in Portsmouth, and although most of the guns on the ship are wooden replicas (to save weight), an original 24pdr Blomefield can be viewed in the grounds of the National Maritime Museum in Greenwich. This very gun was part of the armament of the ship in 1805, and was 'in the thick of things' at Trafalgar. The cast iron barrel with the special naval swelling muzzle has a calibre of 148mm. The length of the gun's barrel to the breech ring is 2904mm, and the pommel with breech tackle ring add a further 261mm, giving an overall length of 3165mm.

The barrel, cast around the year 1800, weighs about 2530kg. The barrel bears the coat of arms of King George III (1760-1820), but is otherwise unembellished.

Danish 12pdr bronze cannon, 1768

Another bronze piece from the series cast in Henrik Hornhaver's Frederiksvaerk in 1768 is this weapon, now belonging to the Orlogsmuseum in Copenhagen.

The barrel, based on the 'Prinz Carl af Hessen' design, was originally intended as an army weapon, like the one just described. In 1861 several barrels of this type, *ie* rifled 127mm muzzle-loaders, were converted for naval use in Denmark, and were set up on two or four-wheeled carriages for use as ships' armament. Here again the reinforce features a high-quality portrait of King Christian VII. The gun illustrated was also part of the armament of the steam frigate *Jylland*.

British Blomefield Pattern Iron 24pdr. (National Maritime Museum Greenwich, Great Britain, INV No. KTP-0029)

The barrel (of the Armstrong type) was manufactured as a solid casting, but was subsequently bored out to a calibre of 14.8cm.

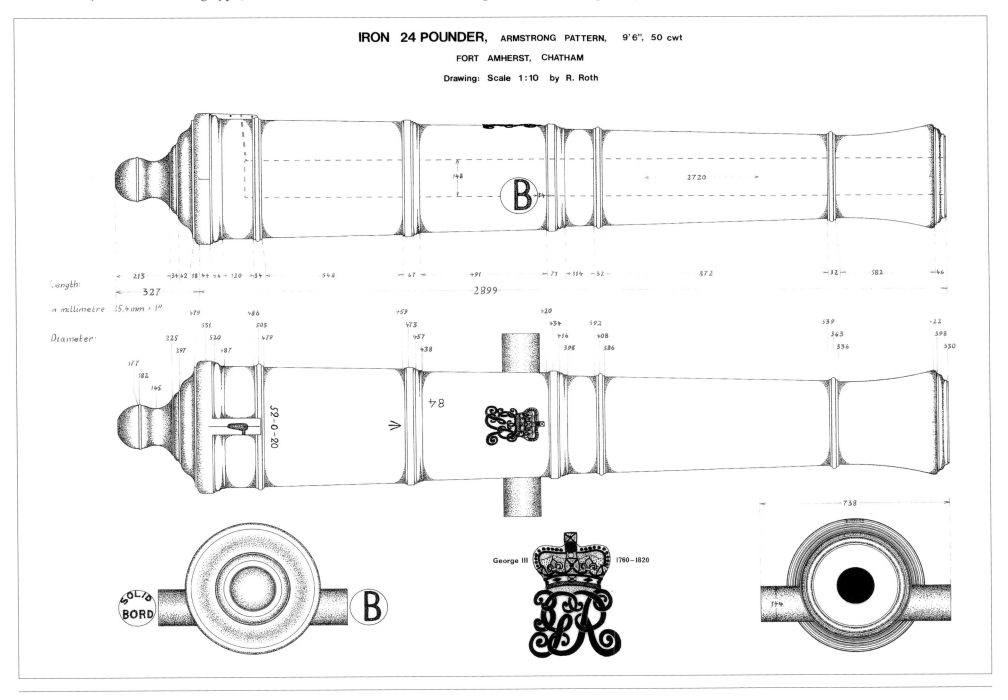

IRON 24 POUNDER, ARMSTRONG PATTERN, 9'6", 50 cwt

FORT AMHERST, CHATHAM

Drawing: Scale 1:10 by R. Roth

George III 1760–1820

SOLID BORD

British Carron 24pdr muzzle-loader, 1797. (Peter Tamm collection, Hamburg, Germany)

British 3pdr muzzle-loader, 1807

This bronze barrel was cast by D. & H. Koong in 1807. On the barrel we find an entwined letter 'M', forming a broad arrow, which is the emblem of Lord Moira, Master-General of the Ordnance. The reinforce bears the coat of arms of King George III. A belt around the escutcheon bears the motto of the Order of the Garter HONI SOIT QUI MAL Y PENSE ('Evil to him who evil thinks').

The calibre of the weapon, shown here mounted as a swivel gun, is 7.4mm. The length of the barrel to the breech ring is 92cm, the overall length including the pommel 99cm, the maximum measured barrel diameter 17.7cm. It is unlikely that the wrought iron swivel yoke shown here is the original mounting.

British Carron 24pdr muzzle-loader, 1797

This cast-iron muzzle-loader, shown here displayed on a simplified reconstructed carriage, was part of the upper deck battery of the British Third Rate ship of the line HMS *Foudroyant* (commissioned 1798). The *Foudroyant* served briefly as Admiral Horatio Nelson's flagship after the Battle of the Nile. The left trunnion (seen from the rear) is engraved CARRON 1797, and on the right-hand side the number 56529 (the Carron Foundry's manufacturing number). The second reinforce is embellished with the insignia of King George III. On both sides of the breech ring are found dotted markings showing three coarse and four fine divisions for adjusting the elevation. In front of the breech, adjacent to the vent field, are two holes for flintlock firing mechanisms. The calibre of this weapon is 14.5cm, the barrel length 282cm, including breech tackle ring 300cm. The maximum diameter at the breech ring was measured at 50cm. This collection includes two further Carron barrels with the same dimensions, dating from 1811 (No. 77737) and 1812 (No. 81178).

British 3pdr muzzle-loader.
(Peter Tamm collection, Hamburg, Germany)

(Museum ship USS Constitution, *Boston, USA)*

From left to right: star shot, bagged grapeshot, canister shot, chain shot, double-headed shot and round shot.

American 24pdr gun on USS *Constitution*

Initially armed with relatively short 24pdr and 18pdr guns, the frigate *Constitution* was fitted with thirty new 24pdrs in 1809, designed to be carried on the gundeck. The gun barrels, manufactured by the Cecil Iron Works of Maryland in 1808, were 2.85m long ('long gun') and weighed 2880kg. They fired solid shot weighing 10.8kg, achieving a range of 1090m (1200 yards) with these projectiles. Operating this weapon called for a crew of twelve men plus a powder boy. A well-trained crew could achieve a rate of fire of 1 round every 3 minutes.

Various types of projectile are on display on board the *Constitution*.

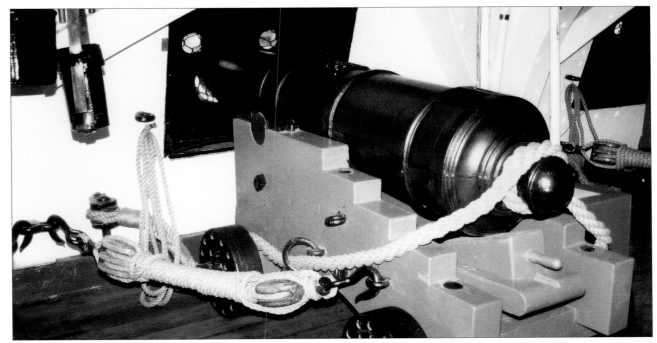

(Museum ship USS Constitution, *Boston, USA)*

French 18mm Espingole, *c*1750

Adopting the principle of the earlier 'organ guns', multi-barrel weapons were also fitted on ships, for close-range combat. The barrels of this seven-barrel weapon are made of bronze, and have a constant calibre of 18mm. The barrels vary in length from 74 to 77cm, and all of them are mounted on a common timber baseplate. A single vent, covered by a hinged plate, allowed the gunner to fire all the barrels at once using a slow-match.

The baseplate is able to swivel and elevate on its mount, and features an annular handle at the breech end. These weapons fired lead balls which had a devastating effect on the decks of enemy ships. The weapon could be tilted up for reloading, which took a crew of two men about 3 minutes

French 18mm Espingole. (Musée de la Marine, Paris, France)

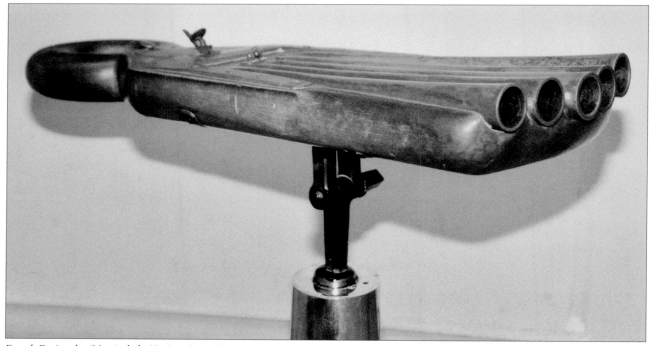

French Espingole. (Musée de la Marine, Paris, France)

French Espingole, *c*1800

This gun is broadly similar to the previous weapon, but features five 'blunderbuss' barrels of equal-length mounted on a baseplate. The barrels flare towards the muzzle, where their calibre is 45mm. This weapon also features a single vent, with an integral flint-lock. These weapons fired musket balls or lead shot, designed to disperse to a limited extent. This weapon also swivels and elevates on its mount, and it was usually mounted on or behind the ship's bulwark.

British ½pdr wall-piece. (Peter Tamm collection, Hamburg, Germany)

British 1½pdr wall-piece, c1780

This swivel gun also features a cast bronze barrel with flintlock firing, but does not feature a reduced-size powder chamber. The calibre is a constant 3.5cm over two-thirds of the barrel length, and expands to 7.5cm towards the muzzle. It seems likely that this weapon fired musket balls or lead shot, as did the blunderbuss itself.

At the rear end of the barrel two firing marks are hammered into the metal, in the form of crossed sabres with a crown set over them. Between the two symbols we find the letter 'P'. What looks like 'HMS Tyme' is carved into the top face of the butt, indicating that the gun may have armed a Royal Navy ship of that name. The length of the barrel is 69.5cm and the overall length including butt is 113cm. Once again the stock and butt are made of walnut, and all parts of the lock are made of iron.

British ½pdr wall-piece, c1800

A wall-piece was a form of swivel gun with a musket-type stock and firing mechanism. Designed for fortress use, they were also employed on small warships and privateers. The cast bronze barrel of this very well preserved example features flintlock ignition. The powder chamber is of smaller bore, and its outside diameter is also smaller. The lock plate bears the royal insignia GR (King George III) and the engraving TOWER (showing it was inventoried at the royal arsenal at the Tower of London). The barrel is of a constant bore of 4.2cm. The length of the barrel including powder chamber is 53.5cm. The stock and butt are made of walnut.

British 1½pdr wall-piece. (Peter Tamm collection, Hamburg, Germany)

Russian 36pdr ship's gun, 1826

This 17cm calibre Russian gun stands today in what is known as the 'cannon yard' of the former Bastion IV on the Malakoff hill in Sebastopol.

Part of the armament for Russian warships of the Black Sea fleet, these guns were removed at the start of the Crimean War in 1853 when the vessels were sunk in the harbour entrance to act as blockships. The guns were then installed, together with their naval crews, in several batteries around Sebastopol. The gun in this picture was manufactured by the Laksid gun works in 1826. During the siege it fired explosive shells as well as grape-shot and case-shot. An eight-man crew was required to work it.

The second picture shows another Russian 36pdr on its original carriage, now on display near the ferry landing in Dublin harbour. At the end of the Crimean War this gun was captured as a trophy by troops of an Irish regiment, and taken home with them.

(see also p66)

(Malakov memorial, Sebastopol, Ukraine)

French 59mm 'Canon Foudre'. (Musée de la Marine, Paris, France)

French 59mm 'Canon Foudre', 1828 model

This is a French 'drum cannon', which holds an interesting place in the history of artillery. Conventional muzzle-loading guns were restricted by their limited rate of fire, and in an effort to increase that rate a series of experimental guns was made, equipped with a carousel of multiple powder chambers that could be pre-loaded.

When one powder chamber had been brought into position behind the end of the barrel, the entire carousel was shifted forward mechanically. This action pushed the (usually conical) mouth of the chamber into the barrel. The horizontal carousel shown here has twelve chambers and could be rotated by mechanical means behind the end of the barrel. The gun also included an elevating screw. The length of the cannon from the muzzle of the barrel to the end of the loading drum is 1.6m (excluding handle). This weapon was constructed in Lyon in 1837, and experiments continued for some time, with constant improvements. The basic disadvantage of this design was the that seal between the chamber and the end of the barrel was not gas-tight, and this eventually caused such experiments to be abandoned.

Russian 1pdr 'Unicorn'. (St. Petersburg naval museum, Russia)

American 12in muzzle-loader, 1840

This 30.5cm smooth-bore muzzle-loader was developed by Captain Robert F Stockton. The weapon was manufactured for the US Navy from forged steel in 1840, and was installed as part of the armament of USS *Princeton*. During a demonstration firing the barrel split and burst, killing one officer, two Congressmen and the US Secretary of the Navy; the result was that the manufacture of forged-steel guns was temporarily halted.

Russian 1pdr 'Unicorn' on naval carriage

In the Russian army and fleet some types of gun – primarily small howitzers – were termed 'Unicorns'. Some European gun names were based on creatures such as 'Snake' or 'Basilisk' and in this case the Russians selected a fabulous creature which was, it was hoped, a symbol for belligerence and courage. The gun, preserved in the St. Petersburg Navy museum together with its original carriage, is a bronze 1pdr with a calibre of 50.8mm.

The barrel was cast in 1843 and features the legendary creatures cast-in as handles. Note the rounded chock on the front of the carriage for better traversing at the gunport.

American 12in muzzle-loader. (Navy Museum, Washington D.C., USA)

British 68pdr shell gun, 1852

This shell gun was placed on display in 1904 to mark the 50th anniversary of the defence of Odessa during the Crimean War. It was originally part of the armament of the British steam frigate *Tiger*. When a Franco-British squadron of thirty-two ships of the line and frigates broke off an unsuccessful bombardment of the town of Odessa on 8 April 1854, the *Tiger* was left behind to watch the port. However, in foggy conditions the ship ran aground near Arkadia, and was subsequently set on fire by a Russian field battery. The Russians later salvaged the ship's guns from the wreck. This cast-iron barrel, on its original carriage, has a calibre of 20.6cm. According to Russian figures the weight of the barrel is 250 Pud (*c*5 tons).

British 68pdr shell gun. (Crimea memorial, Odessa, Ukraine)

French 12pdr muzzle-loader, 1801

This cast-iron muzzle-loading barrel with a calibre of 120mm was salvaged from the Adriatic coast. Nothing is known about its use, although one might speculate that it was booty taken by Croat or Serbian corsairs. Today the barrel, mounted on a reconstructed carriage, is on display at the entrance to the Zagreb shipbuilding institute.

Carronades and mortars

British 24pdr carronade NP. (Royal Armouries Fort Nelson, Portsmouth, Great Britain, Inv. No. XIX – 235)

Dutch 30pdr carronade, 1800

The reinforce of this bronze carronade bears a curved scroll proclaiming MARINE DER BATAAFSCHE REPUBLIK ('Navy of the Batavian Republic'). The cascabel is shaped to the British pattern, with integral breech tackle ring and threaded hole for the elevating screw.

On the breech ring the manufacturer's designation C:SEEST: 1800 can be made out. The calibre of this weapon is 15.5cm, the barrel length 134cm, overall length including cascabel 159cm. The measured diameter at the breech ring is 40.4cm. No details are known of this gun's service life.

British 24pdr carronade, NP 1808

This gun is representative of the basic form of all carronades. The picture shows a 24pdr weapon which was manufactured in 1808 by the Carron Company in Falkirk (Scotland), the foundry which first developed them and gave them its name.

Carronades were based on the ideas of the British General Robert Melville, who suggested that a short-barrelled naval gun with less windage would be especially effective in close-range combat. After initial experiments the guns went into production, and by 1779 quite large numbers of 3pdr, 12pdr and 24pdr carronades were in production. The cast-iron weapon shown has a calibre of 145mm. The barrel includes a cast-in sight piece, and is 1114mm long to the breech ring (overall length 1475mm). At the cascabel is the ring for the breech tackle, with a threaded hole for the elevating screw. The barrel is mounted in the carriage by means of cast-in loops and cross-bolts passing through pivot brackets. The weight of the barrel depicted here is 671.6kg.

Dutch 30pdr carronade. (Peter Tamm collection, Hamburg, Germany)

Cast iron 12pdr carronade, made by the Carron Company in 1805.

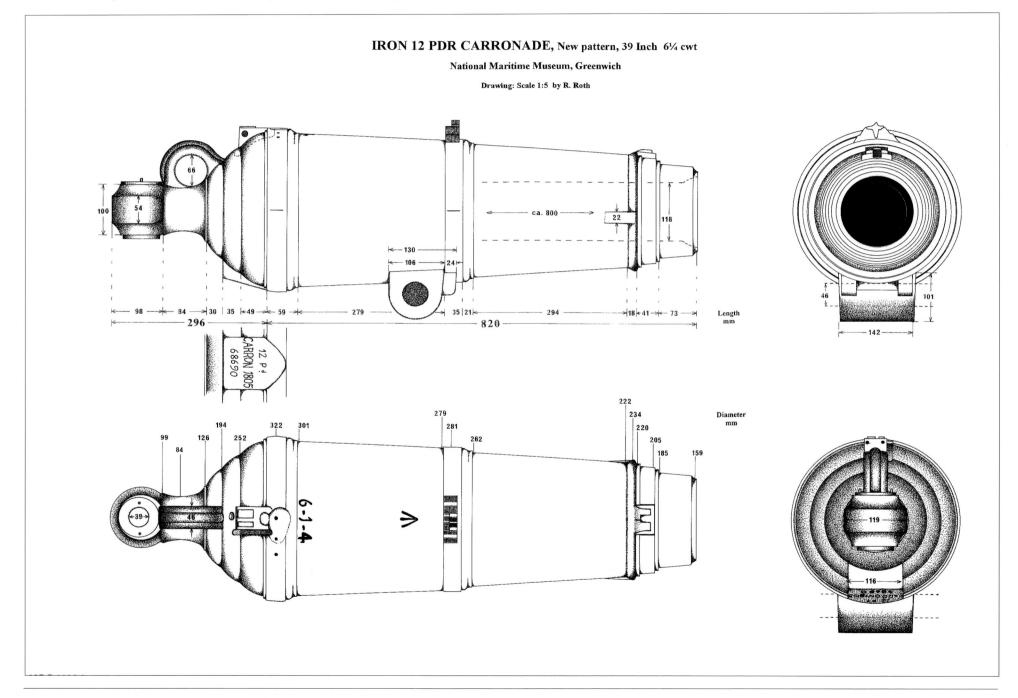

IRON 12 PDR CARRONADE, New pattern, 39 Inch 6¼ cwt

National Maritime Museum, Greenwich

Drawing: Scale 1:5 by R. Roth

American 32pdr carronade. (Museum ship USS Constitution, Boston, USA)

Norwegian 36pdr carronade (see also p66). (Horten navy museum, Norway)

Norwegian 36pdr carronade, 1800

This cast-iron carronade, made by the Fritsoe Werk in 1800, has a calibre of 16.9cm. It was formerly part of the armament of a Norwegian-Swedish sailing warship. The cascabel includes an integral breech tackle ring and elevating screw.

The simple block mount is a reconstruction, and features a semicircular end.

American 32pdr carronade on USS *Constitution*

The US frigate *Constitution* (launched 1797) was first fitted with carronades in 1807, when eight were installed. These guns subsequently proved effective in battle, and as a result the ship was fitted with twenty-four new 32pdr carronades which were mounted on the spar deck in 1809.

The cast-iron barrels were produced by the Henry Foxall Iron Works in Georgetown, Columbia, in 1808. The length of the barrel is 1.21m. In contrast to many carronades employed in other navies, trunnions were cast into these barrels instead of a pivot loop. The maximum firing range is stated to be 360m, but the enemy was usually engaged at much closer range. The gun required a crew of between four and nine men to operate it.

24pdr carronades – archaeological find. (Dänholm naval museum, Stralsund, Germany)

Russian 8pdr carronade, 1820

After 1790 carronades of various calibres were also procured for the Russian fleet, purchased directly from the Carron Works in Scotland. Later, production of these weapons began in the Ishorski works in St. Petersburg in 1800.

The 8pdr carronade shown here has a calibre of 107mm. The bronze barrel, cast at Ishorski in 1820, features an early version of a dispart sight. The cascabel includes an integral breech-tackle ring and also a threaded lug for the elevating screw. In this case the barrel is mounted on the carriage by means of loops cast into the barrel, and cross-bolts fitted through the sides of the carriage.

24pdr carronades – archaeological find

Two of these well-preserved cast iron carronades were discovered at Juliusruh on the island of Ruegen. To date it has proved impossible to determine their date of manufacture and where they served. It seems likely that these weapons were simply left lying where they were found when they were in transit, or perhaps had been intended to be private souvenirs for a collector. In terms of design these weapons appear to be of British origin, and we can assume that they were made around 1800. The measured calibre is 140mm and the barrel length 910mm.

Russian 8pdr carronade. (St. Petersburg naval museum, Russia)

French 12-pouces [inches] mortar, 1700

This so-called 'standing mortar', featuring trunnions cast into the base of the barrel, could be elevated by means of a quoin placed at the central reinforce (the mount is not original). The design for the standing mortar can be traced back to the Dutch military engineer Baron Menno von Coehoorn (1641-1704). The calibre of this mortar is 230mm, with a reduced-diameter powder chamber. The muzzle bears the inscription LUIS CHARLS – Meistre de l'Artillerie. The year of manufacture is also included as A MDCC (1700). In the centre two integral dolphins combine to form a transverse handle. Such mortars were primarily employed on 'galiotes a bombes' (French bomb vessels) and were used in large numbers in the bombardment of Algiers and Tripoli.

British 13in mortar. (Royal Armouries Fort Nelson, Portsmouth, Great Britain, In. Vo. XIX – 196)

British 13in mortar, 1726

10in and 13in mortars were the most common types of high-angle weapons c1700 installed on the Royal Navy's bomb vessels. This bronze 'standing mortar' was cast by A. Schalch in 1726.

The calibre of the barrel is 331mm, and the length including chamber is 1598mm.

French 12-pouces mortar. (Musée de la Marine, Paris, France)

Swedish 20pdr bronze mortar, 1735

This trunnioned mortar was cast by Gerhard Meyer in Stockholm in 1735.

The Swedish fleet employed this type of high-angle weapon on small bomb ketches, and also on the small craft of the inshore fleet. They were also installed in harbour fortifications and forts.

Swedish 20pdr bronze mortar. (Karlskrona naval museum, Sweden)

Cast iron 13in mortar, made by Low Moor in 1856.

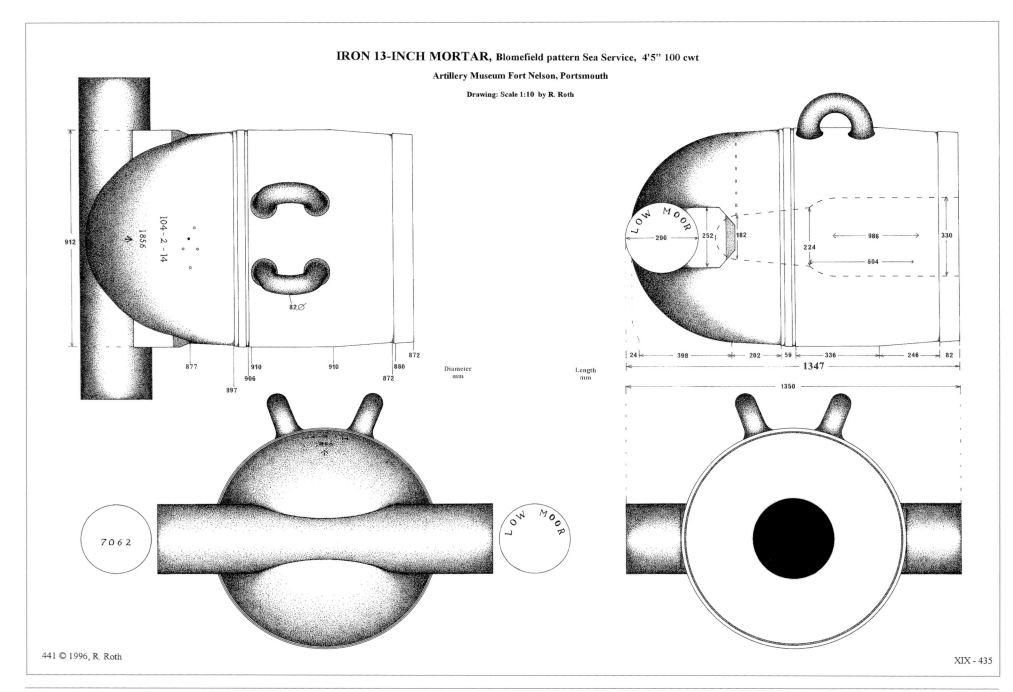

IRON 13-INCH MORTAR, Blomefield pattern Sea Service, 4'5" 100 cwt

Artillery Museum Fort Nelson, Portsmouth

Drawing: Scale 1:10 by R. Roth

XIX - 435

French 60pdr bronze mortar, 1837

The Schemel mortar – the French word is 'mortier' – shown here was cast in Rochefort in 1837. This mortar also features a reduced-diameter powder chamber, and its calibre is 190mm. The angle of elevation is fixed at 45°. According to French information a range of 195 to 243m was possible with this mortar. At this time such mortars were used to fire explosive shells with time fuses. This relatively light mortar could be employed during boat attacks and landing operations.

French 36pdr howitzer, 1786 model

In the French Navy small howitzers were used as an initial response to the British carronade. This weapon, designated 'Obusier de 36', features an integral elevating screw, as fitted to carronades. The angle of elevation does not correspond to that employed for genuine howitzers. The mounting, using a cast-in loop, cross-bolt and mounting brackets, is also similar to the method used on most carronades. The calibre of the bronze barrel is 175mm. Although cylindrical externally, the inside of the barrel also features a reduced-diameter powder chamber. At the rear the barrel displays the engraved letters A/N, and above this is a curved banner proclaiming 'Frimaire [November-December] . Lan . 3 . de la Republique' [1794-5]. Running around the breech ring is further lettering giving the manufacturer as VOUNDERIE D NANTES. According to French information such weapons were employed on ships until about the first decade of the 1800s.

Left: French 60pdr bronze mortar (see also p68).
(Musée de la Marine, Paris, France)

French 36pdr howitzer. (Musée de la Marine, Paris, France)

Rifled breech-loaders and muzzle-loaders up to 1890

American 20pdr muzzle-loader, 1865

At the end of the American Civil War in 1865 this type of rifled muzzle-loader was in production at the gun works of the Washington Navy Yard, intended to arm ships of the Federal fleet. The bronze barrel has three wide rifling grooves. In contrast to the usual practice, the trunnions on this barrel are located at the centreline of the barrel.

The sides of the carriage are also completely of cast bronze construction, with lightening holes stiffened by flanges. A spindle running through the end-piece was provided for adjusting elevation. The recoil was controlled simply by the friction of the plates at the rear of the carriage, and – of course – by the breech tackle.

British Armstrong 7in rifled muzzle-loader. (Horten naval museum, Norway)

British Armstrong 7in rifled muzzle-loader, 1866

Rifled muzzle-loading guns made by the British manufacturer Armstrong & Co. were procured by Norway in the period beginning in 1869; they were required for arming ships, and also for coastal forts. The gun's jacketed-tube barrel – calibre 178mm – is manufactured in four layers, and features six rifling grooves. Originally the barrel was installed in a carriage featuring an Erikson multi-plate brake and wheels. The overall length of the barrel shown here is 330cm, the maximum diameter 79.7cm. The weight of the barrel is stated to be 6.6 t. The gun fired 54.4kg hard cast-iron studded Palliser shot.

American 20pdr muzzle-loader. (Navy Museum, Washington D.C., USA)

Cut-away deck model including Armstrong 7in rifled muzzle-loader, 1866

From 1867 the Austrian Navy also procured thirty-six 7in rifled muzzle-loaders from Armstrong to equip its new ironclad warships. The barrel of these guns was installed in a cheek carriage (Rapert) and set up on a slide mount with Erikson-type multi-plate brakes. Fused shells and hard cast-iron shells were fired, with a maximum range of 3184m at 9.25° elevation. The model shows the arrangement of a single gun together with accessories in the battery deck of the ironclad *Habsburg* (scale 1:20).

Note: the upper deck has a 9cm L/24 bronze gun.

Swedish Wahrendorff 15cm L/21 M 1861 gun

To succeed its 12cm rifled breech-loading guns the Wahrendorff company, based in Aker (Sweden), began to manufacture improved 15cm cannon, and

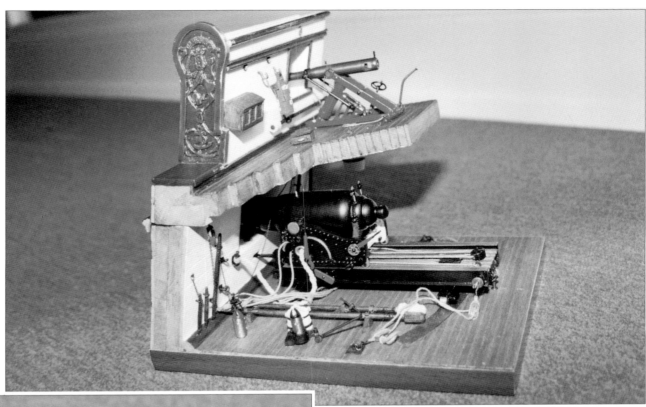

Cut-away deck model showing Armstrong 7in rifled muzzle-loader. (Peter Tamm collection, Hamburg, Germany)

these guns (amongst others) were introduced in large numbers into the Austro-Hungarian Navy. The guns, mounted on slides and four-wheeled carriages, had a cast-iron barrel with 30 rifling grooves. The barrel was fitted with a piston breech, was 3068 mm long, and weighed 2.86 t. The recoil was controlled by a Ferguson-type brake. The range of elevation of the slide carriage was -8° to +14°. These guns fired 27.7kg fused shells amongst other projectiles, and were operated by a crew of 15 men. This type of gun saw service both in the naval action off Helgoland on 9 May 1864, and also in the battle off Lissa in 1866.

Swedish Wahrendorff 15cm L/21 M gun. (Peter Tamm collection, Hamburg, Germany)

British Armstrong 30pdr breech-loader. (Peter Tamm collection, Hamburg, Germany)

British Armstrong 30pdr breech-loader, 1850

This model, to 1:20 scale, represents an early rifled breech-loader made by the British designer G W Armstrong, installed on a slide mount. The breech was of the screw type with opening lever – it did not swing out – and still featured a threaded hole for an elevating screw. Reloading was complicated and time-consuming.

The picture below shows a model of the Russian circular ironclad *Novgorod* of 1874. Armed with 28cm Obuchov guns, she was the smaller predecessor of the *Vice-Admiral Popov* armed with 30.5cm guns, also made by Obuchov. The drawings on the next page also show the arrangement of these 30.5cm guns.

Model by Lothar Wischmeyer. (Peter Tamm collection, Hamburg, Germany)

30.5cm Obuchov gun on hydraulic disappearing mount on Russian circular ironclad *Vice-Admiral Popov*, 1876.

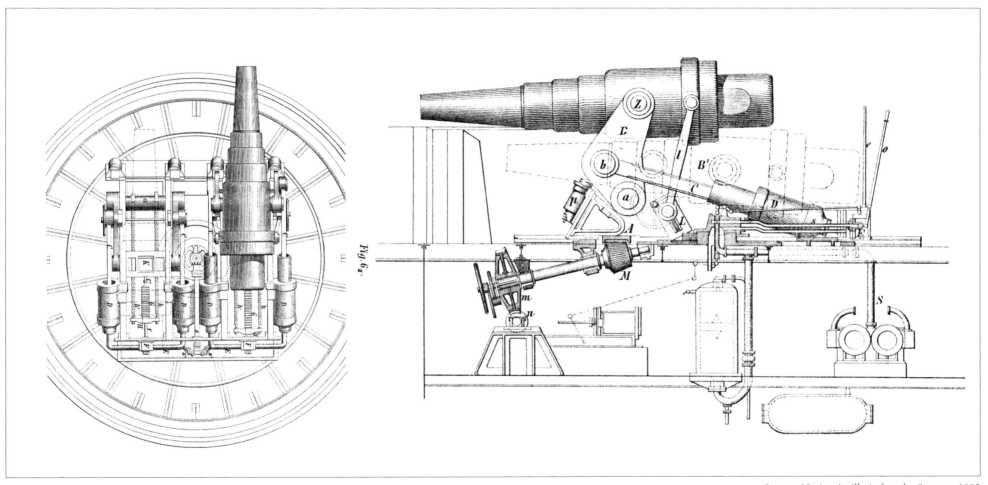

Source: Marine-Artillerie fremder Staaten, 1882

Swedish Finspong 27cm M 76 gun. (Statens sjöhistoriska museum, Stockholm, Sweden)

British Armstrong 40pdr rifled muzzle-loader, 1876

This rifled muzzle-loader was part of a spectacular find of no fewer than eleven gun barrels, made at the time of the restoration and subsequent re-fit of the Hamburg museum sailing ship *Rickmer Rickmers*. This sailing ship was built in 1896, and has a lively history (ex *Flores*, ex *Sagres*, ex *Santo Andre*, ex *Max*).

In 1983, to the surprise of all concerned, the gun barrels mentioned above were found amongst the ballast in the hold of the ship. Presumably these had been installed in the vessel (at that time the *Flores*) by the British in 1917, during the First World War, to act as fixed ballast. The steel jacketed barrel has a calibre of 120mm. The length of the barrel alone is 2.42m, including breech tackle ring 2.56m. The maximum measured diameter is 0.47m. The left trunnion bears the markings SIR W.G. ARMSTRONG & Co. 1878, PREP 88 LB; the right trunnion bears the number 36861 and the calibre 40 P. Only two of these gun barrels remained in Hamburg, all the others being sold to various museums. One example was transferred to the German Naval Weapons school in Mürwik.

Swedish Finspong 27cm M76 gun

This rifled 27cm muzzle-loading gun was supplied to the Swedish Navy by Finspong in 1879. The barrel bears the number 15, and is installed in a mount made by Kockums Mechanical Workshops of Malmö. The recoil of the carriage and barrel was absorbed by hydraulic brake cylinders mounted on the slide. The barrel weighs 24 t. The weapon was installed on the Swedish gunboat *Rota* (launched 1879), which remained in service until 1905.

British Armstrong 40pdr rifled muzzle-loader. (Peter Tamm collection, Hamburg, Germany)

Swedish Wahrendorff 12pdr breech-loader, M 1841

Early breech-loaders with mechanical breeches were manufactured by the Swedish iron foundry of Baron Wahrendorff. This gun is an early example with a smooth-bore barrel, but later models were rifled. The guns were supplied on truck carriages or slide frame mounts. The 12cm cannon illustrated here, bearing barrel No. 284, has a piston breech with locking cylinder. It was made for the Swedish navy in 1845. Elevation was adjusted by means of a wooden quoin.

This weapon was later converted to percussion firing. In the picture the barrel is mounted on its original carriage.

Swedish Wahrendorff 12pdr M 1841 breech-loader.
(Karlskrona navy museum, Sweden)

British Whitworth 18pdr breech-loader, 1860

These rifled 18pdr bronze guns with screw breech were designed by Whitworth & Co. in Manchester. Some of the weapons, including 4pdr and 6pdr examples, were purchased by Denmark from Great Britain for its fleet. A characteristic feature of these barrels was the hexagonal rifling. The barrel is installed in a restored original two-wheeled carriage.

British Whitworth 18pdr breech-loader. (Copenhagen Orlogsmuseet, Denmark)

British Armstrong 110pdr 82-cwt rifled breech-loader. (Museum ship HMS Warrior, Portsmouth, Great Britain)

British Armstrong 40pdr 35-cwt rifled breech-loader

Between 1863 and 1864 four of these 120mm rifled breech-loaders with screw breech were part of the armament of HMS *Warrior*. They were set up on the upper deck at gunports No. 1 and 2 on the port and starboard sides. The carriage recoil when the gun was fired was limited to 20.3cm by the breeching tackle. The weapons fired 18kg shells with a propellant charge of 2.25kg of black powder. The length of the barrel of this weapon is 2.69m and the maximum barrel diameter 41.6cm (overall length 3.03m).

British Armstrong 110pdr 82-cwt rifled breech-loader, 1861

This 17.8cm (7in) rifled breech-loader with screw breech was part of the armament of the British broadside ironclad HMS *Warrior*, commissioned in 1861. The majority of *Warrior*'s original guns were mounted on truck carriages – the ship's armament included forty smooth-bore 68pdrs – but these guns were installed on pivoting slide mounts fitted with metal block brakes. The length of the barrel is 3.04m, and the maximum diameter 0.71m. The barrel weighs 4165kg. These weapons fired 47.2kg heavy armour-piercing shells, capable of penetrating wrought iron plates 196mm thick at close range. This gun is set up as a bow chaser.

British Armstrong 40pdr 35-cwt rifled breech-loader. (Museum ship HMS Warrior, Portsmouth, Great Britain)

Krupp 26cm C.79 gun.

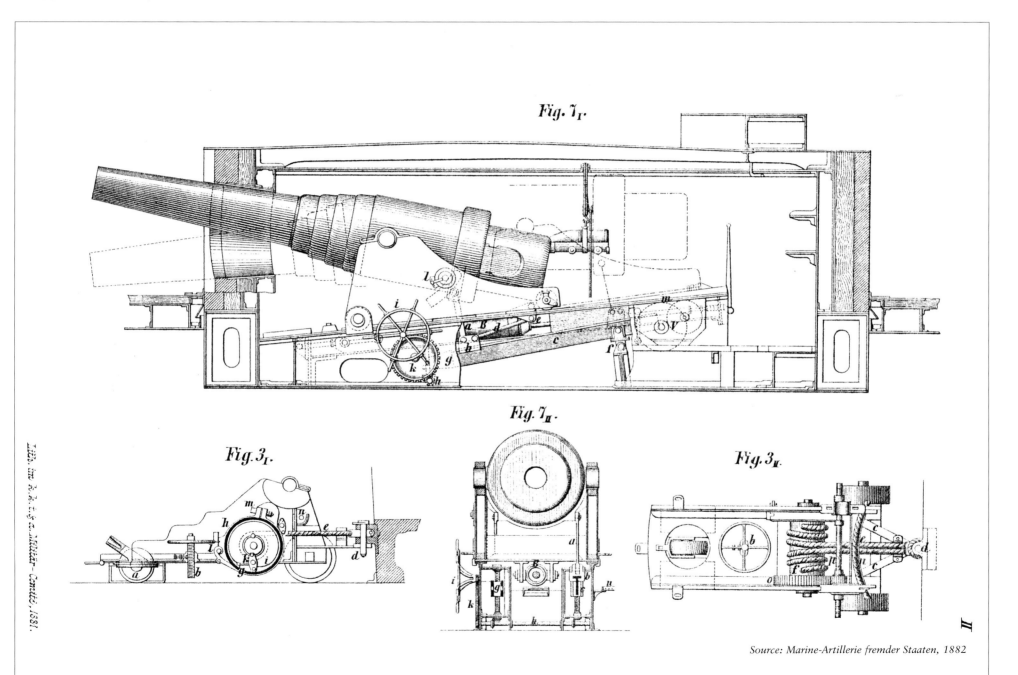

Fig. 7₁.

Fig. 7ᴵᴵ.

Fig. 3₁.

Fig. 3ᴵᴵ.

II

Source: Marine-Artillerie fremder Staaten, 1882

Russian 4pdr battery gun, 1867 model

Beginning in 1867 the Russian fleet was gradually supplied with rifled 4pdr and 9pdr breech-loading guns. The 4pdrs have a calibre of 86.8mm, and were built by the Obuchov works to a design based on drawings supplied by Krupp.

These weapons fired 6.8kg shells – later also case shot – with a range of 4815m at 26° elevation. With a barrel length of 1713mm the original weight of the weapon was 360kg. The recoil of the mount on the timber box frame was controlled by multi-plate brakes. Later versions were installed on steel mounts with hydraulic brake cylinders, based on a design by Baranovski.

By 1879 the Russian fleet had 198 of these weapons. The 4pdr gun shown here was part of the armament of the Tsar's yacht *Dershava*.

Russian 4pdr battery gun. (St. Petersburg navy museum, Russia)

Instructional model of Krupp 30.5cm L/22 C/76. (Copenhagen Orlogsmuseet, Denmark)

Instructional model of Krupp 30.5cm L/22 C/76 gun

The Danish navy launched its armoured ship *Helgoland* in 1878, and as armament the navy selected the 30.5cm C/76 gun made by Krupp. To train the gun crews the company produced the instructional model illustrated here.

The carriage of this gun, which was also installed on German *Wespe* class armoured gunboats, rested on the inclined slide of a pivot mount.

Traverse and elevation were manually operated. The barrel was 6.7m long, was fitted with a horizontal piston breech and weighed 36 t. The weapons fired various projectiles including 329kg C/81 steel shells with a maximum range of 9000m.

(Museum frigate Jylland, *Ebeltoft, Denmark)*

German Krupp 5in breech-loader, 1879

This type of Krupp breech-loader with piston breech was introduced around 1880 to supplement the armament of the Danish steam frigate *Jylland* and the screw corvette *St Thomas*. These weapons were known by the Danish designation 5" 28 Ctnr. B.K., and according to an original drawing their calibre was 127mm in the loading chamber and 120mm at the muzzle. The length of the barrel is exactly 3000mm, and the maximum diameter is 440mm. With an inclined slide mount, hydraulic recoil brakes and pivot bolt arrester, the weapons had an elevation of -7.5° to +13° and a traverse of 80°.

Krupp 5in rifled breech-loader for the Danish frigate *Jylland*, 1880

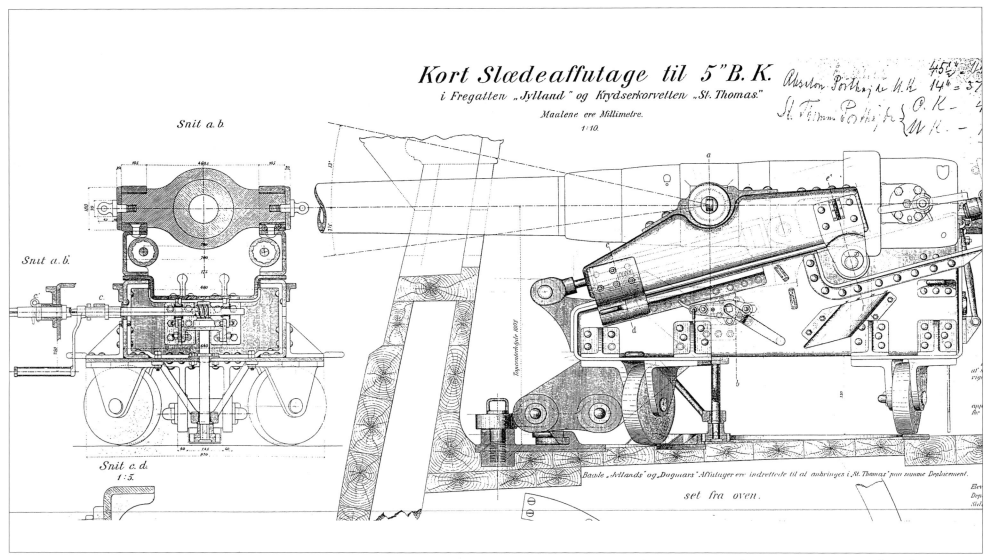

Kort Slædeaffutage til 5"B.K.
i Fregatten „Jylland" og Krydserkorvetten „St. Thomas."

Maalene ere Millimetre.

1:10.

Snit a.b.

Snit a.b.

Snit c.d.
1:5.

set fra oven.

Source: Description of 'Den 5' 28 Ctnr. B.K.', Danish naval ministry, 1899

Swedish Finspong 12cm gun, M 1881

The barrel of this gun, bearing the number 88, was manufactured at Finspong in 1890. The swivel mount bears works No. 4, and was supplied by Friedrich Krupp AG of Essen. As is evident, this weapon featured a mechanically-driven pivot mechanism and was supported on a circular plate by means of four flanged wheels. The gun was part of the modernised armament of the Swedish gunboat *Skagul* (launched 1877).

(Statens sjöhistoriska museum, Stockholm, Sweden)

The third picture (see p58) shows the same weapon made by Finspong (barrel No. 58), but in this case installed on a mount made by Kockums Mechanical Workshops in Malmö.

This gun was installed as part of the armament of the frigate *Wangis*. It was manufactured in 1899 and incorporated some improvements, and the claimed range was 5000m.

German Krupp 8.7cm gun, 1882

In addition to the 5in guns already mentioned, the Danish navy also procured 8.7cm rifled breech-loaders from Krupp. This barrel is 210cm long and features 24 rifling grooves. Complete with piston breech its weight is 502kg. The weight of the fused shell was 6.5kg.

Swedish Finspong 12cm M 1881 gun (see p72).
(Statens sjöhistoriska museum, Stockholm, Sweden)

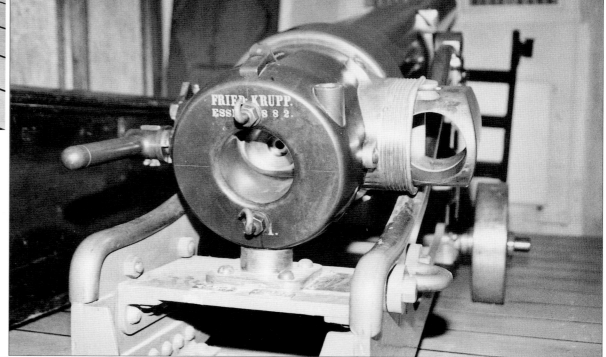

German Krupp 8.7cm gun. (Copenhagen Orlogsmuseet, Denmark)

10in cast muzzle-loader with hydraulically-adjustable trunnion height on British ironclad *Alexandra*, 1877.

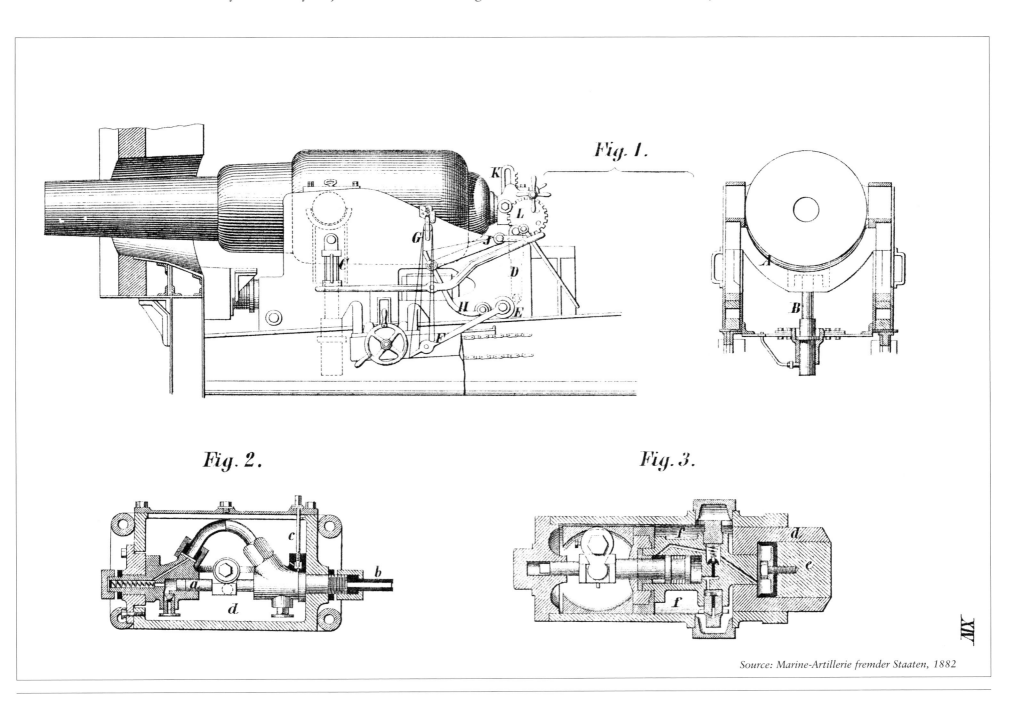

Source: Marine-Artillerie fremder Staaten, 1882

British Armstrong 6in gun, M 1883

This 6in gun with screw breech was built by W.G. Armstrong & Co. in 1884, and was supplied to the Swedish navy in the same year.

The mount, with its inclined recoil bed, was manufactured by the German company Krupp. The barrel has a calibre of 15.2cm, and is 6.7m long. Shells weighing 45.4kg could be fired at a rate of 9 rounds per minute. This gun formed part of the armament of the Swedish First Class gunboat *Disa* (launched 1877).

British Armstrong 6in M 1883 gun.
(Statens sjöhistoriska museum, Stockholm, Sweden)

German Krupp 15cm L/30 built-up gun.

American 5in/40 casemate gun, 1894

The photograph shows a 127mm casemate gun installed on the American armoured cruiser *Olympia*, dating from 1895. This gun, with its screw breech and barrel recoil brake, represents the original ancestor of a long series of developments which by 1941 had embraced more than twenty-five modifications (Mk 1 to Mk 15/4), whilst retaining many of the weapon's basic design elements. The *Olympia* carried ten of these weapons as its secondary armament. The length of the barrel of this model is 5.08m and it weighs about 5 t. The stated maximum range was 11,000m, firing 22.7kg shells.

German Krupp 15cm L/30 built-up gun, 1890

The 15cm L/22 and L/30 built-up guns – exact calibre 149.1mm – were employed as medium artillery on casemate ships of the German navy both on the gun decks and on the upper deck. Up to the C/94 model the weapons were installed on frame mounts with inclined recoil tracks. The L/30 gun was 4470mm long and the barrel had 36 rifling grooves. The end-piece included a horizontal circular wedge breech. Firing 51kg hardened shells the gun was claimed to be capable of piercing 250mm of armour at close range.

American 5in/40 casemate gun. (Museum ship USS Olympia, *Philadelphia, USA)*

Early semi-automatic and automatic weapons, boat guns and landing guns

Swedish Nordenfelt 25mm machine cannon, M 1877

This rifled 4-barrelled weapon, developed by the Swedish engineer Torsten Wilhelm Nordenfelt (1842 – 1920) and the Swedish inventor Palmcrantz, was procured for the ships of the Swedish navy to provide defence against torpedo boats. The semi-automatic weapon had a rate of fire of 120 rounds per minute, with an effective range of 1500m. The gravity-fed mag-

(Istanbul military museum, Turkey)

azine bears the designation 'Batt. Nr. 12'. A worm drive provided rapid traversing, while elevation was adjusted manually. Nordenfelt machine cannon were acquired by many fleets and also produced under licence.

The second picture shows essentially the same weapon with slight modifications, as introduced by the Ottoman Turkish navy for the same purpose.

Swedish Nordenfelt 25mm M 1877 machine cannon.
(Karlskrona naval museum, Sweden)

British-Swedish Palmcrantz-Nordenfelt 25mm machine cannon (see also p193). (Wehrtechnisches museum, Koblenz, Germany)

British-Swedish Palmcrantz-Nordenfelt 25mm machine cannon

This 25.4mm machine cannon, purchased for the Germany navy c1880, was manufactured in Nordenfelt's London factory.

French Hotchkiss 37mm revolving cannon, 1895

This 5-barrelled revolving cannon of French manufacture was produced for the Spanish navy in the Hotchkiss works at Saint Denis in 1895. It was captured in 1898 during the Spanish-American war, and brought to the USA as a trophy. This type of weapon – amongst others – was employed in the Spanish navy as anti-torpedo boat artillery. Only the weapon itself has survived, without its mount and pedestal.

Russian Hotchkiss system 37mm revolving cannon

In 1875, Russia imported its first series of multi-barrel 'quick-firing cannon' with calibres of 25.4mm to 44.4mm, intended to be mounted on various classes of ship as defence against torpedo boats. In 1886, after comprehensive testing, Russia paid 200,000 Francs for the licence to build 37mm and 44mm Hotchkiss cannon. The barrels of these weapons were initially produced at the Obuchov works, while the weapons were assembled and completed at the Tula weapons factory. By 1896 the Tula works had already produced 290 revolving cannon of both calibres. The length of one barrel of the 37mm gun is 740mm, the overall length of the weapon 1485mm. The practical firing rate is given as 80 rounds per minute, and the effective range around 2700m.

The weapon illustrated here was built in 1889, by which time the guns were manufactured completely at Tula. These guns first saw action on Russian ships during the Russo-Japanese war of 1904-5.

(Navy Museum, Washington D.C., USA)

(St. Petersburg naval museum, Russia)

French Hotchkiss 3.7cm revolving cannon purchased by the German navy.

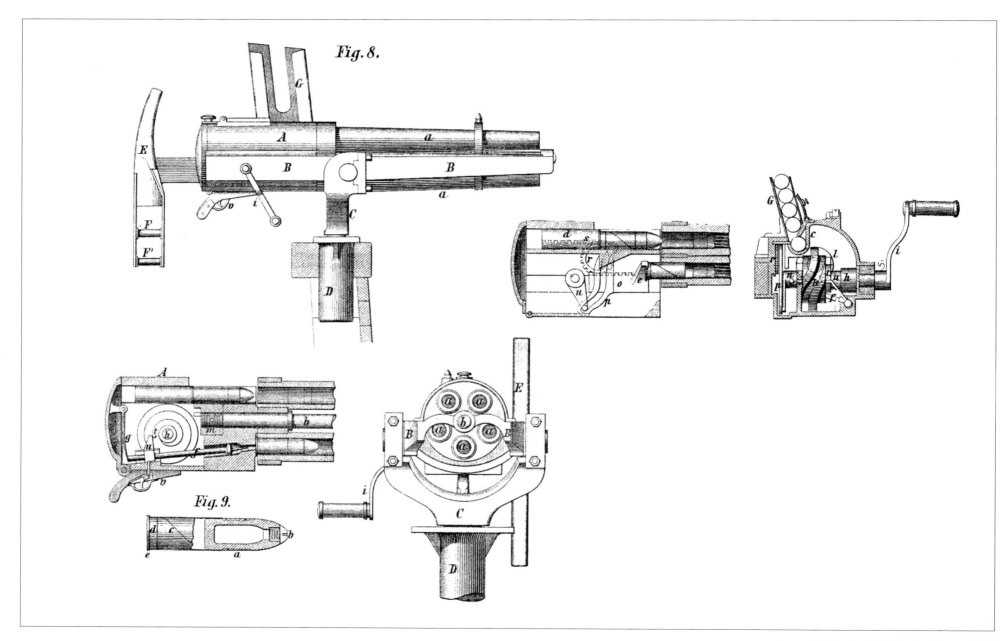

Source: Marine-Artillerie fremder Staaten, 1882

Danish 24pdr muzzle-loader, 1631.
(Copenhagen Orlogsmuseet, Denmark)

Swedish 24pdr muzzle-loader, *c*1670.
(Kalmar castle, Sweden)

Russian 36pdr ship's gun, 1826.

Norwegian 36pdr carronade, 1800.
(Horten naval museum, Norway)

Dutch 2pdr chamber piece, *c*1730.
(Peter Tamm collection, Hamburg, Germany)

British Armstrong 4pdr muzzle-loader, from Captain Cook's *Endeavour*.
(National Maritime Museum, Sydney, Australia)

French 60pdr bronze mortar, 1837.

Swedish 7-tommes L/10.5,
M 1838 shell gun.

In the foreground: Obuchov 6in/35 gun, 1885.

German 28cm SK L/54.4 C/34.
(Austråstt museum battery, Orlandet, Norway)

Swedish Bofors 7.5cm L/50 M/12 deck gun.

(Bofors industrial museum, Karlsgoga, Sweden)

British 6in Mk XI deck gun, 1914.

(East Point Military Museum, Darwin, Australia)

Russian Obuchov 12in
L/52 MA 1907 naval guns.

('Maxim Gorki I' armoured battery,
Sebastopol, Ukraine)

Swedish Finspong 12cm M 1881 gun.   *(Statens sjöhistoriska museum, Stockholm, Sweden)*

British Maxim-Nordenfelt 3.7cm machine cannon, 1904.

(Istanbul military museum, Turkey)

British Maxim-Nordenfelt 3.7cm machine cannon, 1904

This 3.7cm machine cannon was produced in London after the merger of the armaments manufacturers H. Maxim and Th. Nordenfelt. Supplied from 1904 to the Ottoman Turkish navy, this type of weapon was employed both for torpedo boat defence and also as armament on torpedo boats and patrol vessels. Mounted on a pedestal (weapons No. 2006) the gun was traversed and elevated manually.

A screw allowed the operator to set a fixed elevation. The length of the barrel including water-cooled bronze jacket and breech is 1870mm. The cartridges were fed to the gun in canvas belts. With a muzzle velocity of 550m/s a firing rate of 300 rounds per minute was obtained.

British Maxim-Nordenfelt 3.7cm machine cannon (see also p72).
(Istanbul military museum, Turkey)

German Maxim-Nordenfelt 3.7cm machine cannon, 1903

This machine cannon was manufactured for the German navy in 1903 by the German weapons and munitions factories in Berlin. The barrel, bearing the works No. 581, is 1110mm long, while the overall length of the weapon is 1850mm. The barrel has 12 rifling grooves with a right-hand twist. Once again the ammunition feed took the form of a textile belt on the right-hand side.

German Maxim-Nordenfelt 3.7cm machine cannon. (Berlin-Spandau fortress museum, Germany)

American 5.5in boat gun. (Museum of American History, Washington D.C., USA)

American 12pdr boat howitzer, 1871

This smooth-bore 12pdr muzzle-loader was also designed by John A. Dahlgren in 1862, and its intended purpose was as a boat gun and landing gun. The weapon was designated a howitzer, and was manufactured by the Washington Navy Yard in 1871, and equipped the steam frigate USS *Kearsarge*. The gun barrel bears the number 168, and weighs 191kg. The stated maximum range was 910m.

American 5.5in boat gun

This gun was developed by John A. Dahlgren (1809-70), for gunboats and sloops of the USN. The bronze barrel, bearing the number 62, weighs 583kg, and its calibre was measured at 14.5cm. The barrel features an elevating screw, and is mounted on a timber slide. The front pivot bolt and two trucks on the end of the slide allow the gun to be traversed.

American 12pdr boat howitzer. (Navy Museum, Washington D.C., USA)

Russian 2.5in landing gun, M 1882

This 63.5mm calibre landing gun was built in the Obuchov works in 1896. The gun was designed by W.S. Baranovski in 1882, and features an early form of recoil-control mechanism with a mechanical spring brake. In 1897 the gun formed part of the equipment of the coast defence battleship *Admiral Ushakov* (commissioned in 1896).

The gun fired 0.8kg explosive shells with an effective range of 2800m. It was termed a 'light gun', and weighed only 272kg. Its rate of fire was stated to be 5 rounds per minute. This type of landing gun was also employed on land in the Russo-Japanese War, firing shrapnel shells.

Russian 2.5in M 1882 landing gun. (St. Petersburg naval museum, Russia)

American 3in Mk 4 landing gun. (Navy Museum, Washington D.C., USA)

American 3in Mk 4 landing gun

This 76.2mm landing gun was manufactured by the Bethlehem Steel Corp. in 1900. This type of gun formed part of the equipment of American capital ships and cruisers, and features a form of barrel recoil brake and recuperator. The gun shown in this photograph was used during the landing of American troops at Vera Cruz in 1914, during a period of unrest in Mexico.

American 3in Mk 11 landing gun. (Navy Museum, Washington D.C., USA)

German 10.5cm gun from SMS *Königsberg*

This 10.5cm gun was part of the armament of the German light cruiser *Königsberg* (commissioned 1907), which on 11 July 1915 was scuttled in the Rufiji delta in former German East Africa after suffering damage from British shellfire. All the guns were removed by the crew and mounted on wheeled carriages (wheels with rod spokes) in the railway workshop of Dar es Salaam, some of them made by the crew members.

Four carriages with cast wheels were then quickly fabricated in Germany – see photograph – and these were successfully landed by the supply ship *Marie* (*Sperrbrecher* 15) in March 1916. All these guns saw service in the battles in East Africa of the German forces under General von Lettow-Vorbeck. The gun in the picture now stands at Fort Jesus in Mombasa (technical and ballistic data as for SMS *Emden*).

American 3in Mk 11 landing gun

This gun is a further development of the Mk 4 model. The elevation was increased, and the gun was fitted with a shield to protect the crew from small-arms fire. This model was also carried on board many battleships and cruisers of the US Navy in the period between the World Wars.

German 10.5cm gun from SMS Königsberg.
(Fort Jesus, Mombasa, Kenya)

Quick-loading and quick-firing guns up to *c*1920

American 3pdr Mk 15 deck gun

Apart from 6pdr (57mm) guns the US Navy also employed a series of 3pdr (47mm) guns on pre-dreadnoughts and armoured cruisers from around 1895, for torpedo boat defence. For this role, 3pdr guns by Hotchkiss, Vickers and Nordenfelt were pressed into service, amongst other types. The 47mm gun illustrated was produced by Driggs Seabury in 1916 as armament for new 66ft submarine chasers. The single-shot weapon has a vertical sliding breech block and barrel recoil brake. Traverse and elevation were entirely manual. 1.49kg shells were fired with a maximum range of 6220m. The gun required a three-man crew.

French 47mm torpedo boat gun, M 1905

This single-shot gun with shoulder support was produced by the French manufacturer Schneider-Canet, and formed part of the artillery armament of the Bulgarian torpedo boat *Draski* (commissioned 1907). Six boats of this type were built in Varna in the period 1907 to 1908, with French materials and assistance. The guns were for the defence of the boat, and were also installed on several French torpedo boats and torpedo boat destroyers.

The gun shown weighs 270kg, and the ammunition was 1.5kg explosive shells. With a three-man crew a rate of fire of 10 rounds per minute could be achieved.

French 47mm M 1905 torpedo boat gun.

(Varna navy museum, Bulgaria)

American 3pdr Mk 15 deck gun. (Navy Museum, Washington D.C., USA)

This gun equipped several classes of Russian battleships, armoured cruisers, cruisers and gunboats, as well as the famous First Class cruisers *Aurora* and *Diana*. By 1921 Obuchov had manufactured 547 guns of this type, and Perm had produced 248.

Russian Obuchov/Canet 75mm L50 gun. (St. Petersburg naval museum, Russia)

Russian Obuchov/Canet 75mm L50 gun, 1891

In 1891 Russia acquired a licence to build French 152mm, 120mm and 75mm guns of the Canet type. The 75mm/L50 guns were produced, with slight modifications, at Obuchov and also in the Perm gun foundry. Although they only had a moderate performance initially, their range was gradually increased from 6400m to 9150m. The standard deck gun had a maximum barrel elevation of only 25°, but a new mount providing 70° elevation was soon designed and introduced. Initially the gun could only fire 4.9kg armour-piercing shells, but after 1905 fragmentation, high explosive and shrapnel shells were produced for it.

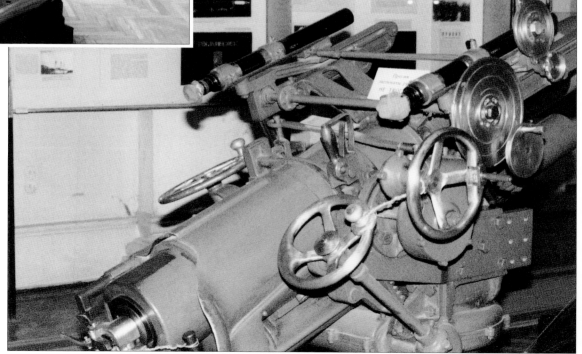

Swedish Bofors 7.5cm L/50 M/12 deck gun (see also p71). (Bofors industrial museum, Karlsgoga, Sweden)

Swedish Bofors 7.5cm L/50 M/12 deck gun

This 7.5cm gun, barrel No. 49, was made by Bofors for the Swedish navy in 1919. The weapon was mounted on a number of different ships, including as anti-torpedo boat guns on the coastal battleship *Sverige*, and also on the torpedo boat destroyers of the *Wrangel* class (4 x 7.5cm). The length of the barrel including breech is 3.75m. The weapon has a vertical sliding block breech, with recoil brake and recuperator mounted below the barrel. The gun could fire various types of projectile, among them 6.6kg armour-piercing shells, with a muzzle velocity of 828 m/s.

German Krupp 8.8cm gun

The severely damaged 8.8cm gun on a centre pivot mount shown in this photograph came from the German light cruiser *Hela*, which was sunk after being torpedoed by the British submarine *E 9* in the North Sea in 1914. The barrel, fitted with a horizontal sliding block breech, is 3080mm long. The barrel weighs 1270kg including the breech. The weapon was salvaged by divers from the wreck of the *Hela*, and today stands in Fort Kugelbake as a memorial to the dead.

(Fort Kugelbake, Cuxhaven, Germany)

The 8.8cm gun was employed in large numbers on German torpedo boats in the First World War.

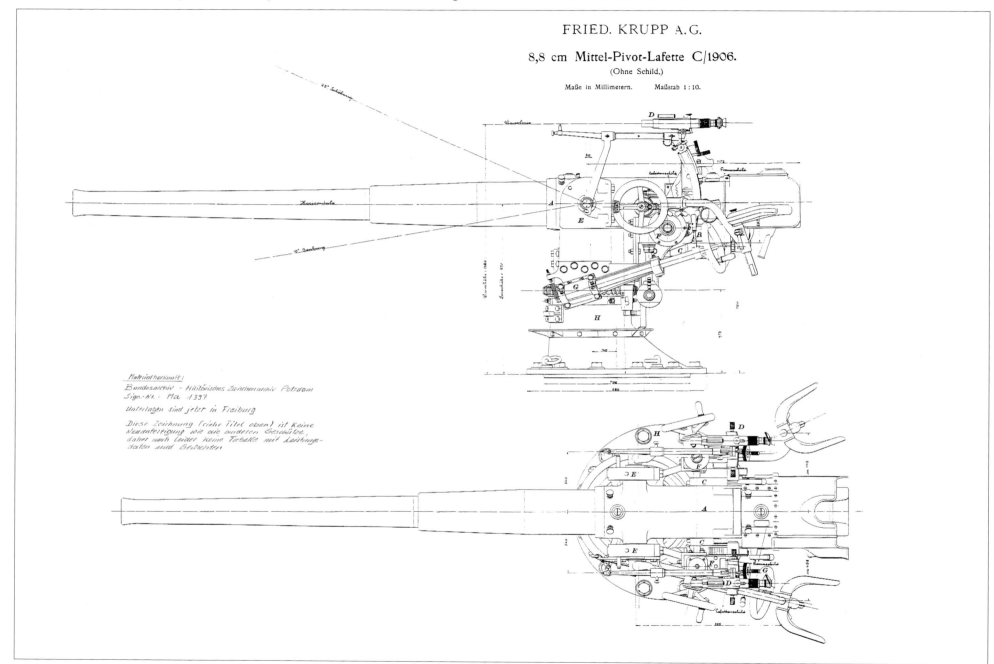

Source: Krupp archive/Federal archive, Freiburg

American 4in/40 cal. QF breech-loader. (Navy Museum, Washington D.C., USA)

British 4in QF gun Mk V

This 101.6mm calibre deck gun – shown here mounted on the destroyer HMS *Walker* ('W' class) – was the standard weapon on many ships of the Royal Navy up to the outbreak of the Second World War. Installed on different mountings, and with barrel elevations of up to 80°, the gun was also employed as anti-aircraft armament on cruisers and aircraft carriers. A total of 920 guns of the various versions was produced. In its Mk V variant, fitted to destroyers of the 'V' and 'W' classes, the weapon weighed 2.13 t. The jacketed barrel and breech had an overall length of 4.77m, and the maximum elevation was 30°. A range of 12.6km at 30° elevation was claimed. Earlier versions of the gun fired separate ammunition (shells, 14.06kg), but fixed ammunition was used with the AA version.

American 4in/40 cal. QF breech-loader, 1890

This 101.6mm calibre gun with a screw breech was manufactured by the Gun Factory of the Washington Navy Yard in 1890. It was employed as the secondary armament on a number of vessels, amongst them the monitors of the *Arkansas* class (1899) and the ships *Puritan*, *New York* and *Columbia*. The barrel is 4.11m long and weighs 1500kg. It had a rate of fire of 10 rounds per minute.

British 4in QF Mk V gun.

German Krupp 10.5cm L/45 gun, C/1904

This gun, on display on a centre pivot mount in Hyde Park in Sydney, formed part of the armament of the German light cruiser *Emden*, which was severely damaged off North Keeling Island on 9 November 1914 by the Australian cruiser *Sydney*. The ship ended up aground on a reef. Three years later three of its guns were salvaged from the wreck to be set up in museums. The weapon shown here bears the works No. 408 and was manufactured by Friedrich Krupp AG in Essen. The gun fired several types of projectile including 14kg armour-piercing shells (charge 5.8kg) with a muzzle velocity of 951 m/s. The stated range was 12,200m at 30° elevation. The barrel is 5.0m long, and it weighs 1755kg. Today the

German Krupp 10.5cm L/45 C/1904 gun. (Hyde Park, Sydney, Australia)

American 4in/50 Mk 9 deck gun. (ANZAC Park, Darwin, Australia)

two other guns from the *Emden* are on display at the naval base at Sydney and the Australian War Memorial in Canberra.

American 4in/50 Mk 9 deck gun

Displayed in the ANZAC Park in Darwin, this 101.6mm calibre gun is a memorial to the sinking of the US destroyer *Peary* (DD 226) during the Japanese air attack on Darwin on 19 February 1942. Ninety-one crew members lost their lives when the ship went down.

There were 24 versions of this gun and it served as armament on most American destroyers from 1914 to 1920 (*eg* the Flush Deckers). This very low-profile mount had a maximum elevation of only 20°. It fired 14.9kg shells (propellant charge 6.58kg NC) to a range of 14.5km, with a muzzle velocity of 884 m/s. The weight of the barrel is around 5 t.

German Krupp 10.5cm L/45 C 1916 torpedo boat gun. (Peter Tamm collection, Hamburg, Germany)

German Krupp 10.5 cm L/50 Utof gun

This weapon was part of the armament of the German torpedo boat *G 102*, which was turned over to the USA in 1920. After the guns had been removed, the boat was sunk as a target during bomb trials near Cape Henry on 13 July 1920. This gun, introduced from 1916, fired 16kg shells with a muzzle velocity of 940 m/s. The length of the barrel is 5.52m. Traverse and elevation were manual.

German Krupp 10.5cm L/45 C 1916 torpedo boat gun

This gun, manufactured by Friedrich Krupp AG of Essen, was part of the armament of the German torpedo boat *V 25* which sank off the island of Borkum after hitting mines. The massive barrel is equipped with a vertical sliding block breech (works No. 742). A special feature of this weapon's design is that it does not include any drive system for elevation. The barrel and breech block was so well balanced that elevation could easily be adjusted by hand, using a training lever. All components of the traversing drive system are made of bronze. A telescopic sight was used to aim the weapon, coupled with the aiming quadrant. The length of the barrel is 4.74m. The hydraulic recoil brake is on top of the barrel, and an open metal spring in the mount served as recuperator.

German Krupp 10.5cm L/50 Utof gun. (Navy Museum, Washington D.C., USA)

Swedish Bofors 12cm L/44 M/94 deck gun

The 12cm screw breech gun shown in the photograph is one of a series which was manufactured by Bofors with calibre lengths of L/44, L/45 and L/50. The weapons were mounted as secondary armament on the Swedish coast defence ships *Thor*, *Njord* and *Oden* (1898-99), and also on a number of torpedo boat destroyers. Six examples were also supplied to Norway in 1894 for its warships. The barrel weight including breech is 2.8 t. With a muzzle-velocity of 740 m/s the gun could fire 21kg armour-piercing shells and penetrate a 22cm thickness of armour at close range. The gun was operated by a 6-man crew.

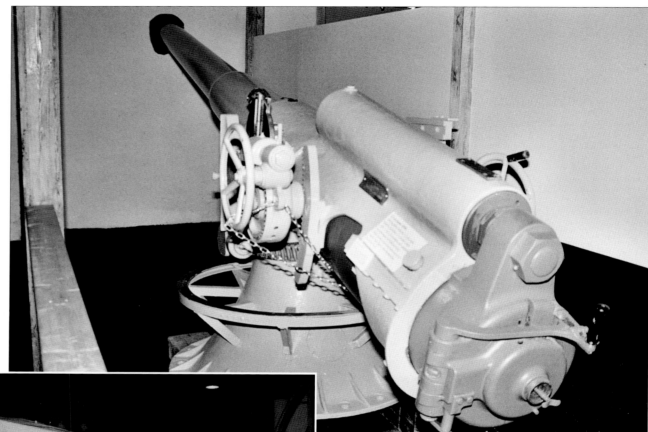

Swedish Bofors 12cm L/44 M/94 deck gun. (Bofors industry museum, Karlskoga, Sweden)

American 5in Mk 15 gun, 1918

These 127mm calibre guns had been developed before the First World War, and were built in large numbers in 25 versions by various manufacturers. Starting in 1918, the 5in/51-calibre gun was installed on destroyers and battleships as anti-torpedo boat artillery. The US Navy's first aircraft carrier, the USS *Langley*, was also equipped with these guns.

With a barrel length of 6.4m the complete weapon weighs around 11 t. The maximum range was 14,500m at 20° elevation firing an armour-piercing shell weighing 22.7kg.

American 5in Mk 15 gun. (Navy Museum, Washington D.C., USA)

American 6in/40 cal. deck gun. (Navy Museum, Washington D.C., USA)

Austrian Skoda 15cm d/50 gun, 1899

This 15cm gun, now on display in the Military History Museum in Prague, is a representative of a long line of development. With constant improvements these weapons were carried by capital ships and armoured cruisers of the Austro-Hungarian navy. The calibre is 149.1mm, and the barrel of the L/50 model is 7860mm long. The gun was used to fire armour-piercing and high explosive shells weighing 45.5kg, and also shrapnel, and was originally fitted with a shield. The rate of fire was given as 10 rounds per minute.

American 6in/40cal. deck gun, 1890

This 152.4mm gun with screw breech and inclined recoil mount with hydraulic brake cylinders was part of the armament (6 x 6in) of the armoured cruiser (or Second Class battleship) USS *Maine*, which was commissioned in 1895. The ship sank after an explosion in Havana harbour on 15 February 1898, and the wreck was raised in 1912.

The barrel is 6530mm long. With an 11.3kg propellant charge the weapon fired armour-piercing shells weighing 45.4kg, and was aimed manually by its eight-man crew.

Austrian Skoda 15cm d/50 gun. (Prague military history museum, Czech Republic)

Russian 6in L/45 gun, Canet model

In 1891 there began a period of close co-operation between the French gun manufacturer Forges et Chantiers de la Méditerranée and various Russian armaments manufacturers. One part of this venture was the production of 75mm and 120mm guns, the other to procure licences to manufacture the 152.4mm Canet type guns (by the St. Petersburg metal works, Perm gun works, Obuchov and Putilov). The Obuchov works alone produced 135 of these 6in guns in the period 1897 to 1901. This weapon (barrel No. 329), which is today mounted as the bow gun of the First Class cruiser *Aurora*, was built by the Obuchov steel works in 1901. Originally all fourteen of her guns were on open centre pivot mounts, but they were later fitted with shields. During the Second World War all the 15cm guns were removed and deployed in coastal and field batteries, or on armoured trains. After the war the ship was refitted with her guns, although not all the original weapons had survived and other examples which had been in storage replaced them.

The barrel plus breech is 6858mm long. These guns were used to fire various types of separate ammunition; the shells were improved over time. Amongst them were 41.4kg L/3.6 shrapnel shells containing 15.9mm balls (each weighing 21.3g). In 1907 the guns were found to be capable of a range of 14km with high explosive shells. This increased to 18km after modernisation and improvement of the shells. The weight of the complete gun is 14.6 t, and it was operated by an 11-man crew.

Russian Canet 6in L/45 gun. (Museum ship Aurora, *St. Petersburg, Russia)*

British 6in Mk XI deck gun (see also p71). (East Point military museum, Darwin, Australia)

British 6in Mk XI deck gun, 1914

This 152.4mm gun was part of the armament of the Australian cruiser HMAS *Brisbane* (commissioned 1916) during the First World War. Removed from the ship after the war, it was set up, together with three other guns of the same type, as a coastal battery at Fort East Point near Darwin, one of the 121 medium-calibre coastal batteries which had been built in Australia by the outbreak of the Second World War. These weapons were capable of a range of 13.4km at their maximum elevation of 30°. They fired armour-piercing and high explosive shells weighing 43.3kg (14.9kg cordite charge) at a rate of fire of 8 rounds per minute. The barrel bears the works No. 2310 and the breech the designation VSM 1914. The guns remained in service until 30 June 1960.

German Krupp 15cm SK L/45 casemate gun, 1909

This 15cm SK L/45 gun, installed in a C/1906 centre pivot mount, was manufactured by Krupp in 1909, and was one of fourteen casemate guns equipping the German battleship SMS *Ostfriesland* (commissioned 1911). The ship was handed over to the USA after the First World War, and was sunk during bombing trials on 21 July 1921. This gun, weighing 5020kg and with a barrel length of 7100mm, had previously been removed.

The recoil brake and recuperator are under the barrel. Various types of projectile were fired, including armour-piercing shells weighing 46kg (propellant charge 16.6kg), and training and elevation were manual. Originally the mount was protected by an armoured shield for use in a casemate.

German Krupp 15cm L/45 casemate gun. (Navy Museum, Washington D.C., USA)

German Krupp 15cm SK L/45 gun, 1911

This 15cm barrel is from a casemate gun installed in a C/1906 centre pivot mount, from the Turkish battle cruiser *Yavuz Sultan Selim* (ex-German *Goeben*, commissioned 1912). The jacketed barrel features 48 rifling grooves, and with the breech weighed a total of 5720kg. The length of the rifled part of the barrel is 5095mm. The casemate armour shield is 80mm thick. Various types of projectile were fired, including armour-piercing and high explosive shells weighing 46kg, at a rate of 7 rounds per minute. Many of the weapon's essential fittings are no longer present.

German Krupp 15cm SK L/45 gun. (Ankara military museum, Turkey)

American 7in/50 cal. Mk 2. Mod. 3 gun. (Navy Museum, Washington D.C., USA)

American 7in/50 cal. Mk 2 Mod. 3 gun

This 17.8cm calibre gun was made in 1913 by the Gun Factory of the Washington Navy Yard, and formed the secondary armament of American pre-dreadnought battleships, and also armoured cruisers. The gun was produced in large numbers up to version Mk 14/1. Some guns remained in use into the Second World War as coastal artillery, and as armament on auxiliary ships.

Swedish Bofors 15cm L/45 gun, 1920

Today this 15cm gun is a memorial in Frederikshaven-Süd. The weapon was originally part of the armament of the Danish coastal battleship *Niels Juel* (commissioned 1923, 10 x 15cm), when it was fitted with a three-sided shield. In addition to Holland and Poland, Denmark purchased more 15cm guns from Bofors to equip its coast defence ships. In the period after 1943 some of these guns were also installed in German coastal batteries. The barrel, bearing works No. 13 and year of manufacture 1922, weighs 6.1 t. It was capable of a range of 17,800m with 45.8kg armour-piercing shells.

Swedish Bofors 15cm L/45 gun, 1920.

British 7.5in/45 cal. Mk II. (Museum ship Georgios Averof)

British 7.5in/45 cal. Mk II, 1907

The photograph shows one of the four 190.5mm twin turrets on the Greek armoured cruiser *Georgios Averof*. The ship was built in 1907 by the Italian Orlando yard, and was subsequently sold on to the Greek navy in 1910. These 7.5in guns were also fitted to some Italian armoured cruisers and the Mk V and Mk VII variants to British armoured cruisers. The length of the barrel including breech is 8.86 m, and the weight of one barrel around 14 t. It could fire a shell weighing 91kg to a range of 18.7km at 30° elevation.

Swedish Bofors 25cm gun, 1899

This gun, formerly mounted singly in a turret, was part of the armament of the Swedish coastal battleship *Njord* (Panzerbaet 2nd class, launched 1898). The barrel is 10.5m long, and weighs around 29 t. The mount was constructed by Finspong in 1898. Hydraulic brake cylinders controlled the recoil. Various types of projectile were used, including armour-piercing shells weighing 204kg; range was 8300m.

In 1930 Bofors also supplied improved weapons of the same calibre for use on the Finnish coast defence ships *Ilmarinen* and *Väinämöinen*.

Swedish Bofors 25cm gun. (Karlskrona navy museum, Sweden)

Part of the barrel of a German Krupp 28cm SK L/45 gun

The picture shows the centre section of a 28cm barrel, bearing the barrel No. 194, which was formerly mounted in the port twin turret on the German battle-cruiser *Seydlitz* (commissioned 1913).

These jacketed-barrel weapons, made by Krupp, were installed in a C 1910 turret mount. The original barrel was 17.3m long, and weighed 77.6 t. The guns fired L/3.2 shells weighing 305kg, fitted with M 6017.1 base fuses. They were capable of a range of 19.2km, and had a muzzle velocity of 850 m/s. The damage to the barrel was caused by a ricocheting British 13.5in shell during the Battle of Jutland on 31 May 1916.

Part of the barrel of a German Krupp 28cm SK L/45 gun. (German naval museum, Wilhelmshaven, Germany)

British Vickers 12in Mk X gun.

British Vickers 12in Mk X gun, 1907

Several classes of British battleships and early battle-cruisers were fitted with 12in (30.5cm) guns as early as 1897, installed in twin turrets. The pre-dreadnought battleship classes only had two turrets, but the number rose to five with HMS *Dreadnought*. The barrels, built by Vickers and Armstrong-Elswick, were variously 14.1 to 15.6m long, and the weight of a single barrel was around 58 t. The Mk X weapon fired various types of projectile, including armour-piercing shells weighing 385kg, with a propellant charge of 161kg of cordite. The rate of fire was 2 rounds per minute. The photograph shows a 12in barrel being replaced on HMS *Agamemnon* in Malta harbour in 1916.

Krupp 30.5cm gun on C 1912 turret mount on the German battlecruisers *Derfflinger* and *Lützow*.

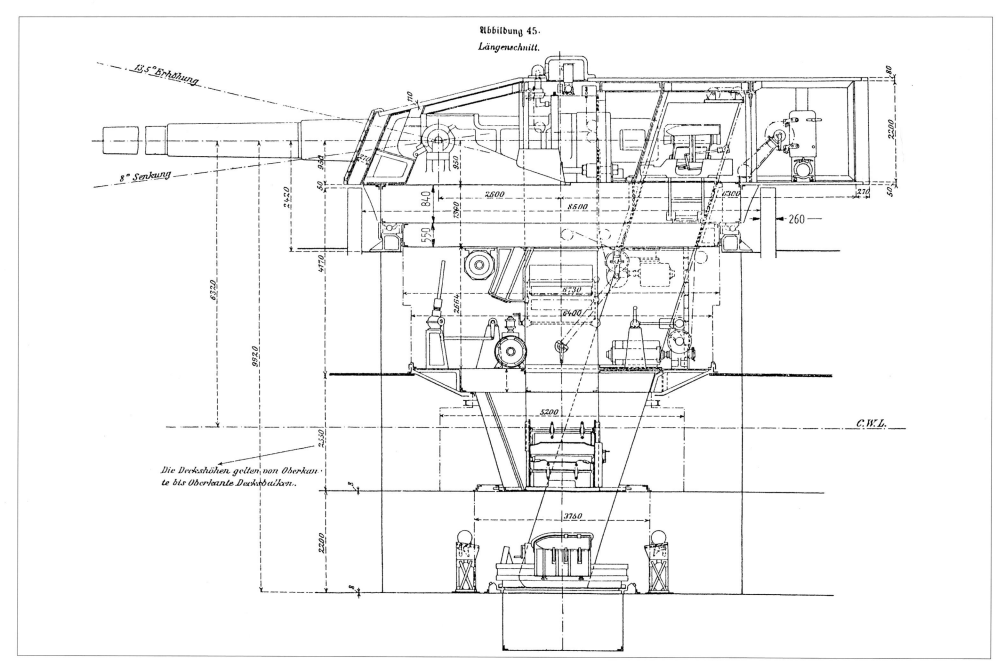

Source: Entwicklung unserer Marineartillerie 1910 bis 1912

(Imperial War Museum, London, Great Britain)

British 15in Mk I gun barrels

The 38.1cm gun barrels on display in front of the Imperial War Museum in London reflect an interesting part of the history of British naval artillery. These weapons were the subject of constant development in the period starting in 1911, and a total of 186 examples were manufactured for use on ships and in coastal batteries.

The left-hand barrel (seen from the rear), bearing the number 125, was originally installed in one of the twin turrets on the battleship HMS *Ramillies* in 1916. After firing in action off North Africa and in the battle off Cape Spartivento (1940) the barrel was removed in 1941 and placed in reserve. The right-hand barrel, No. 102, was made in 1915 and originally installed on HMS *Resolution*. After many practice firings and one period of active service in the Graeco-Turkish war of 1920, it was removed and placed in reserve in 1938. In 1943 it was brought back into service, and installed on the monitor HMS *Roberts*. In 1944 it saw constant action in support of the Normandy landings (D-Day). The gun barrels are equipped with screw breeches, and each barrel weighs around 100 t.

The length of the barrel including breech is 16.5m. The guns fired armour-piercing and high explosive shells weighing 879kg with a muzzle velocity of 749 m/s. A barrel elevation of 30° gave a maximum range of 34.6km.

British Vickers 15in Mk I/N RP

A version of the 38.1cm Mk I/N RP 12 turret was provided for the Royal Navy's last and largest battleship, HMS *Vanguard* (commissioned April 1946) from arsenal stocks (the former turrets of HMS *Glorious* and *Courageous*). The picture shows the ship's 'X' and 'Y' turrets in 1960, when the vessel was already in the breaker's yard at Faslane.

British Vickers 15in Mk I/N RP gun.

Austrian Skoda 30.5cm L/45 gun, 1910

In 1910 new 30.5cm guns were designed for the latest battleships of the Austro-Hungarian navy by Skoda at Pilsen. The four battleships of the *Tegetthoff* class were equipped with two triple turrets forward and two aft on the centreline, and the guns featured electric-powered training. The gun barrels were 13.72m long, and took the form of cantilever jacketed-tube barrels with a horizontal sliding block breech and hydraulic cylinder recoil control. The weight of one barrel and breech was 54.25 t. The range of elevation was initially

-4° to +20°, but this was reduced to just -3.5° to +15.5° after the guns were converted to a linked-barrel configuration. The guns fired various types of projectile including armour-piercing shells weighing 450kg, with a range of 22km at 20° elevation (after conversion: 19km/16°).

A complete turret weighed 678 t. The photographs show the installation of the gun barrels in the aft super-firing turret of *Viribus Unitis* in Pola, and the same ship at sea in 1912.

German Krupp 38cm SK L/45 gun, 1912

All German battleships built after 1913 were fitted with 38cm guns as their main armament. The gun barrels, developed by Krupp in the period starting in 1912, were basically of the same construction as the 30.5cm weapons, but the jacketed-tube barrel was made of burst-proof 'L-steel' and featured only one layer. Barrels up to No. 34 had 100 V-shaped rifling grooves with a depth of 3.8mm. From barrel No. 35 some design modifications were introduced, and after barrel No. 43 a thicker core barrel was used; for these barrels parallel rifling grooves were again adopted. The weight of one barrel and breech was 77.5 t (barrel and cradle 105 t). The maximum range with 750kg armour-piercing shells was 20.4km at 16° elevation (later improved to 23.2km at 20°), and a rate of fire of 2.5 rounds per minute was possible. The newly developed twin turrets had a maximum armour thickness of 350mm. This picture shows the forward turrets of SMS *Bayern* (commissioned 18 March 1916).

The battleship Bayern *at sea on 2 May 1916.*

Deck and turret guns of the Second World War

German 10.5cm SK L/45 C/32 nS

This gun, installed in a C/32 g.E. centre pivot mount made by the Rheinmetall company, was part of a consignment of German weapons delivered to Finland in 1942 as military aid. Several of these guns were set up there in coastal batteries, with AA searchlights and range-finders. This type of gun was also employed on fleet torpedo boats, minesweepers, MPFs (artillery lighters) and other ships of the Germany navy.

(Peter Tamm collection, Hamburg, Germany)

The barrel is 4705mm long (rifled section 3649mm). The maximum range was 15,175m, firing 15.1kg explosive shells (anti-aircraft ceiling was 9300m at 70° elevation). The weight of the complete turret including gunshield is 6750kg. Apertures with folding shields for two telescopic sights are arranged on the front panel. Each gun was also fitted with a separate C/37 or C/38 fuse setter.

Description and drawings of the German Rheinmetall 10.5cm C/32 nS gun; delivery documents for Finland 1942.

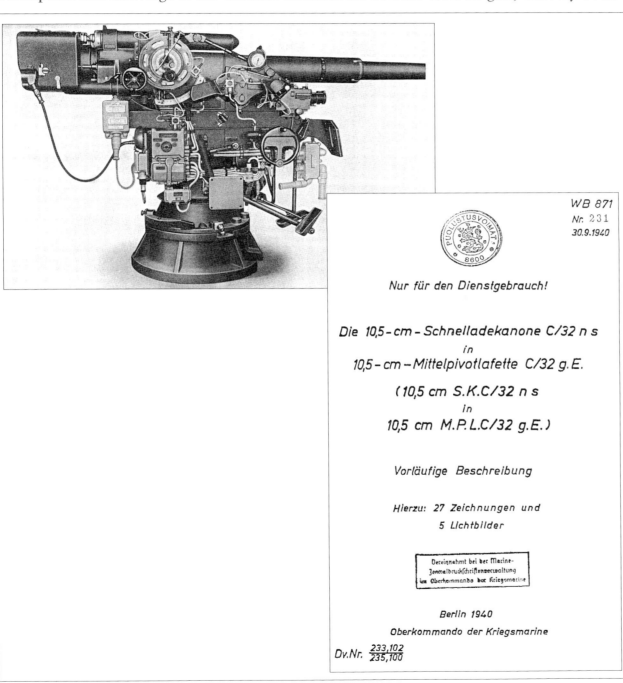

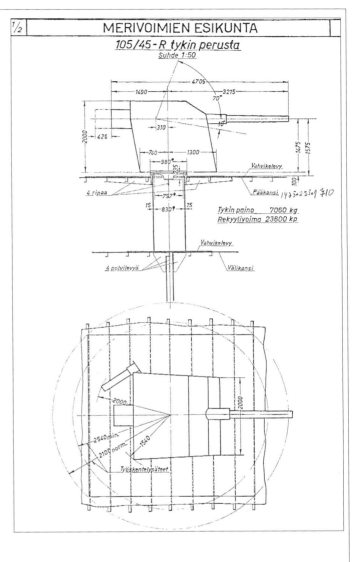

British 4in Mk XIX dual-purpose gun

The development of these 101.6mm weapons can be traced back to before the First World War. In twin and single shielded mounts they were employed on many ship classes of warship in the Royal Navy and Commonwealth fleets, including use as anti-aircraft guns. This example, on display in the park of a military base in Toronto, was part of the armament of Canadian 'Tribal' class destroyers. With a maximum barrel elevation of 80° the weapons were used as dual-purpose guns on destroyers and frigates. The barrel, complete with vertical sliding breech block, is 4231mm long. With a muzzle velocity of 396 m/s the guns could fire 15.8kg shells to a maximum range of 8870m. No fewer than 2023 of the Mk XIX were manufactured, 1006 of them in Canada, 801 in England and 219 in Australia.

(Toronto Park, Canada)

Italian OTO 100mm L/47 M gun.
(Museo Tecnico-Navale, La Spezia, Italy)

overall length of one barrel is 4985mm, and the complete turret weighs around 15 t. The maximum range with 13.8kg explosive shells was 15.2km.

Italian OTO 100mm L/47 gun, M 1937

The 100mm gun with shield is the single-mount variant of the Skoda M 1910 gun, copied and modified. These weapons were employed on the Italian corvette *Ibis*, and they also armed the torpedo boats of the *Spica* and *Cigno* classes. The older M 1931 model had an elevation range of only -6° to +45°. As of 1935 this gun was superseded by new models with a range of -6° to +60°. The ballistic data of these weapons is very similar to those of the twin guns made by OTO.

Italian OTO 100mm L/47 gun, M 1928

The twin mount illustrated here formed part of the armament of the Italian cruiser *Raimondo Montecuccoli* (commissioned 1935). These 100mm guns with horizontal sliding breech blocks were modified versions of the Skoda 100mm M 1910 (several of the Austro-Hungarian ships transferred to Italy in 1920 were fitted with this model). With an elevation range of -5° to +80° these weapons were employed as anti-aircraft guns on the battleships of the *Cesare* class as well as on several cruisers. On older destroyers they were employed as dual-purpose armament. The 1928 model had variable-height trunnion bearings. Earlier models were completely manually operated, but later versions (M 1935/37) were fitted with pneumatic rammers. The

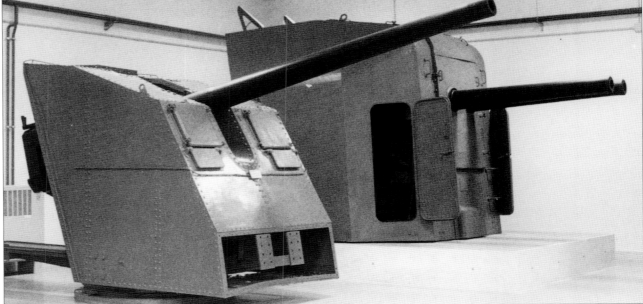

Italian OTO 100 mm L/47 M gun. (Museo Tecnico-Navale, La Spezia, Italy)

Soviet 100mm L/56 OBR. 1937 deck gun

This semi-automatic gun, a development of the 100mm B-34, came into use on various classes of Soviet cruisers, frigates and coastal defence ships. With 15.8kg explosive shells (fixed ammunition round weight 43.5kg) – a range of 22km was possible. Used as AA guns with 85° elevation their ceiling was 15.6km. The gun was operated by an eight-man crew and the rate of fire was 15 rounds per minute. The shield is 6mm thick. It is also worth mentioning that the well-known 100mm Pak BS-3 was derived from this naval weapon in 1943, virtually 'overnight'.

Soviet 100mm L/56 OBR. deck gun, 1937.
(Odessa memorial park, Ukraine)

British 4.5in Mk IV dual-purpose gun

This 114mm gun – exact calibre 113.03mm – was part of the armament of the four *Bergen* class destroyers (British 'Cr' class, 1944/45) supplied to the Norwegian navy after the Second World War. The weapon is in an open-backed gunshield with an armour thickness of 13mm. The weight of the complete turret is 46.3 t. The barrel and breech are 5378mm long overall. The weapon featured a revolving loading mechanism with hydraulic rammers for fixed ammunition (shell weight 24.9kg). Rate of fire was 10 rounds per minute, and maximum range 18,970m. Their anti-aircraft ceiling was 12,500m at 80° elevation.

British 4.5in Mk IV dual-purpose gun. (Horten naval museum, Norway)

Spanish Vickers Carraca 12cm L/45 deck gun, 1929

This gun, manufactured under licence from Vickers at Carraca in 1929, formed part of the armament of Spanish *Sanchez-Barcaiztegui* class destroyers (thirteen ships, 5 x 12cm). The barrel including screw breech is 5.69m long. Training and elevation were manual. The high explosive shell weighed 22kg (propellant charge 6.5kg). Maximum range was given as 11km.

(Castillo de Montjuich military museum, Barcelona, Spain)

German 15cm C/36 torpedo boat gun on TL. C/36. First installed on German Type 1936 A destroyers.

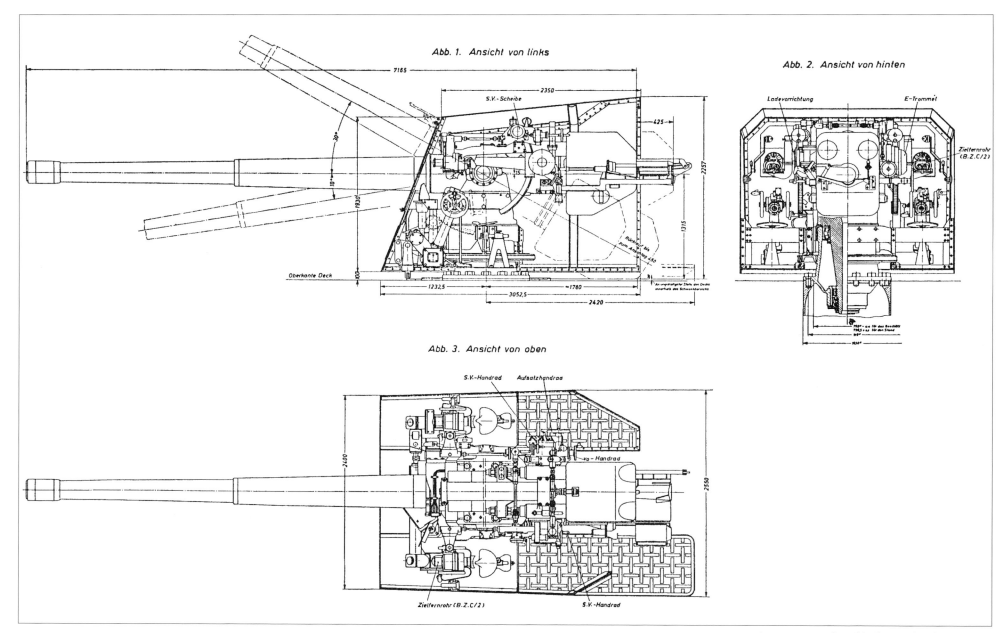

high explosive shells. With a maximum elevation of 30° the range was 19,400m. The complete gun weighs 20.5 t. The *Gryf* was sunk in Hela harbour on 3 September 1939 during a German air raid, but three turrets and 40mm AA guns were salvaged, and were subsequently used in the defence of Hela until the Polish surrender.

Swedish Bofors 12cm L/50 M 34/36 gun. (Gdynia naval museum, Poland)

Swedish Bofors 12cm L/50, M 34/36 gun

This gun, shown here fitted with a 7mm shield, formed part of the armament of the minelayer *Gryf* (commissioned 1938), which was built in France for Poland. The Polish destroyers *Blyskawica* and *Grom* were also equipped with it (3 x 2, 1 x 1). The semi-automatic gun featured both mechanical and electrical firing systems. The barrel including breech is 6390mm long. The rate of fire was 18 rounds per minute with 24kg

American 5in 38 cal. Mk 37 Mod. 6 deck gun

The picture shows the 127mm stern gun of the American Liberty Ship *Jeremiah O'Brien*. This weapon, weighing 184 t, was made by the Northern Ordnancy Incorp. in Minneapolis in 1942, and is one of a large series of such guns. It features combined electro-manual training and an electro-hydraulic shell feed. The barrel is 4.45m long. The rate of fire with 31.5kg shells was 15 rounds per minute (range 23,690m). Maximum elevation was 85°, making it a useful anti-aircraft weapon. By 1945 this gun had been produced in 133 variants.

(Museum ship Jeremiah O'Brien, *San Francisco, USA)*

American 5in/38 cal. Mk 30 deck gun.

USS Hughes.

American 5in 38 cal. Mk 30 deck gun

These 127mm Mk 30 guns form part of the armament of the *Fletcher* class destroyer USS *Cassin Young* (commissioned 1943). Originally the ship carried five of these guns, weighing around 18 t each. Arming a number of American destroyer classes, this was almost the standard gun of its type. Seventy-nine variants of the Mk 30 alone had been manufactured by January 1945. The barrel, 4.82m long, had a braked recoil of 0.38m when fired. Firing 24.9kg explosive shells the gun had a range of 16.6km with a muzzle velocity of 792 m/s. The AA ceiling was 11.3km at 85° elevation. The gun was operated by a twelve-man crew.

USS *Hughes* (commissioned 21.9.1939), a destroyer of the *Sims* class, was equipped with three 5in/38 cal. guns in enclosed gunhouses and two in an open mount.

After the Second World War both turrets were transferred to the newly built Stevnsfort on the island of Seeland, where they served as coastal artillery. In the 1980s they were taken out of service, but have been kept ready for firing to this day by reservist gun crews.

The 149.1mm barrels are 8200mm long, and the elevation range is -10° to +40°. Firing 45.5kg explosive shells the maximum range was 23km at 40° elevation. The rate of fire was 1 round every 7.5 seconds.

(Stevnsfort, Seeland island, Denmark)

German Rheinmetall-Borsig AG 15cm SK L/55 C/28

These 15cm twin turrets, on a C/34 rotating mount, are now on display at Stevnsfort on the Danish island of Seeland. They were originally fitted to the German battlecruiser *Gneisenau*, which was severely damaged by aerial attack in Kiel in 1942. After the ship was decommissioned, two of these turrets were set up as coastal guns on the Danish island of Fano, and placed under the command of MAA 518. By 1944 the guns were ready for use as 'Graadyb Battery', which was also known as 'Gneisenau Battery'.

German 15cm SK C/28 in 15cm C/34 turret. Secondary armament on the German battlecruisers *Scharnhorst* and *Gneisenau*.

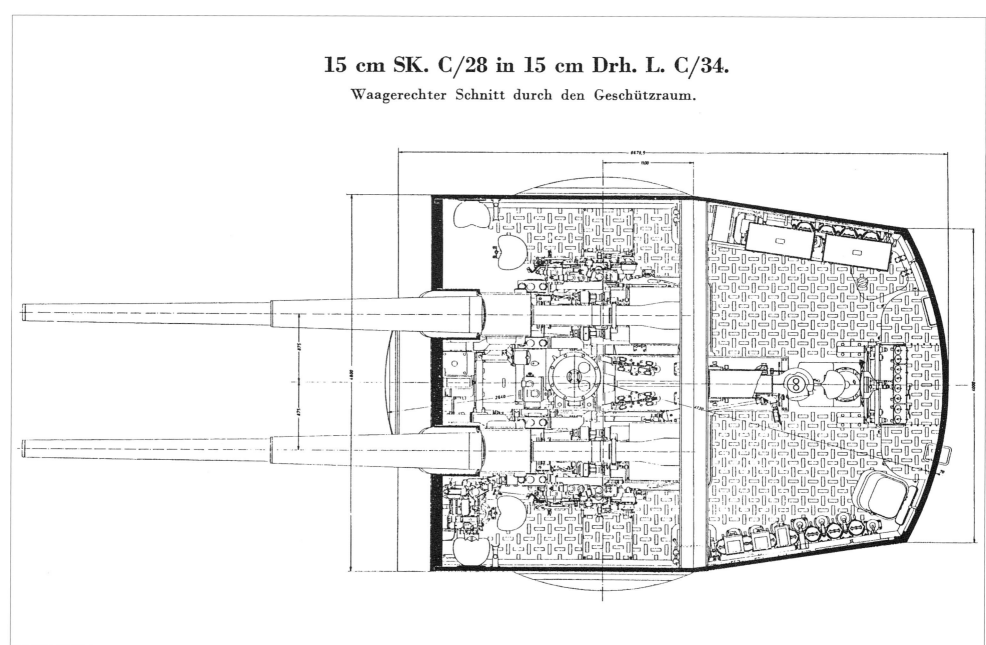

15 cm SK. C/28 in 15 cm Drh. L. C/34.

Waagerechter Schnitt durch den Geschützraum.

German Rheinmetall 15cm SK C/25 gun.

German Rheinmetall 15cm SK, C/25

These 149.1mm guns, installed in triple C/25 turrets developed by Rheinmetall after 1925, were supplied to the three new light cruisers *Köln*, *Karlsruhe* and *Königsberg*, as well as the cruisers *Leipzig* and *Nürnberg*. On the 'K' class cruisers the after turrets were offset to port and starboard by 2m, but on the *Leipzig* and *Nürnberg* they were on the centreline. All barrels could be elevated individually or all together, with an elevation range of -10° to +40°. The barrels were fitted with manually-operated vertical sliding block breeches, and were 9080mm long (axis spacing 1.55m, barbette diameter 5.7m). The traverse was electrically-powered, while the elevation system was hydraulic. Firing 45.5kg shells (muzzle velocity = 960 m/s) the maximum range was 25.7km at 40° elevation. When firing at elevations above 20° the gun had to be run back before it could be reloaded. The rate of fire was 7 rounds per minute. The picture shows the after turrets of the *Leipzig* (commissioned 8 October 1931).

British 6in/51 Mk XXIII in Mk XXIII triple turret

These photographs show the forward turrets of the cruiser HMS *Belfast* (commissioned 1939), each with three 152.4mm guns. A noteworthy feature of these turrets is the position of the central barrel (barrel C), which is 0.76m further back than the other two barrels. This allowed the three barrels to be mounted closer together, with an axis spacing of 0.98m, creating space in the turret for three shell lifts and one cartridge lift. The barrels are 7.86m long.

British 6in/51 Mk XXIII in Mk XXIII triple turret. (Museum ship HMS Belfast*, London, Great Britain)*

(Museum ship HMS Belfast, *London, Great Britain)*

The guns fired 50.8kg shells at a rate of 6 rounds per minute per barrel. They were usually fired in salvos, and had a maximum range of 23.3km. Each turret has front armour plating 100mm thick, and 50mm at the sides, con-tributing to a total turret weight of 178 t. A total of 469 of these guns were manufactured in various versions. The *Belfast* participated in the sinking of the German battlecruiser *Scharnhorst* in 1943 by firing starshell.

(Photo: Imperial War Museum, London)

Soviet 180mm SK MK-3-180 gun. (St. Petersburg, Russia)

Soviet 180mm SK Mk-3-180, 1938

These 180mm triple turrets formed part of the armament of the Soviet cruiser *Kirov* (commissioned 23 September 1938). The guns are a development of the L/60 calibre type for the cruiser *Krasny Kavkas* after 1931 (1 barrel per turret). The barrels are 10.3m long. They fired armour-piercing shells weighing 97.5kg, propelled by a 37.5kg charge, with an elevation range of -4° to +50°. With a theoretical rate of fire of 5.5 rounds per minute, they were capable of a maximum range of 37.5 km. The turret armour is 70mm thick at the sides and front, and 50mm on the roof. Each turret was equipped with a 6m base range-finder.

The weight of one complete turret is 247.4 t. The guns of the *Kirov* and other ships of the Baltic fleet took part in the defence of the besieged city of Leningrad in 1941.

Soviet 'Molnija-AZ' range-finder cupola, 1939

Various types of range-finding apparatus and fire direction systems were developed after 1933 for controlling the heavy guns fitted to a new series of Soviet cruisers. This range-finder is on display in Sebastopol, and was manufactured in the 'Elektropribor' works in 1939. It was part of the fire-direction system of the 180mm triple turrets of the cruiser *Slava* (ex-*Molotov*, commissioned 14 June 1941). It features three 6m base rangefinders which were coupled with the 'Gorisont II' fire direction system. The cupola weighs 19.7 t (plus wiring system, 26.2 t).

Soviet 'Molnija AZ' range-finder cupola. (Sapun Heights museum, Sebastopol, Ukraine)

German Krupp 20.3cm SK C/34 guns

Krupp supplied 20.3cm guns in C/34 twin turrets for the five heavy cruisers of the Kriegsmarine. The ships *Blücher*, *Admiral Hipper* and *Prinz Eugen* were commissioned, but *Seydlitz* and *Lützow* were not completed (the latter was sold to the Soviet Union in 1940). The gun turrets of the *Seydlitz* were eventually used as coastal artillery in France. The jacketed-tube barrels, fitted with hydraulically-operated horizontal sliding breeches, were 12.15m long and weighed 20.7 t. The axis spacing was 2.16m and the barbette diameter 6.40m.

The guns' elevation range was -10° to +37°. The superfiring turrets were equipped with a 7m range-finder. The maximum range with 45.5kg shells (fragmentation, armour-piercing, armour-piercing/explosive) was 33.5km at 37° elevation, and the rate of fire was 12 rounds per minute. The picture shows the after turrets of *Prinz Eugen* at Gotenhafen in April 1941. Note: the 7m rangefinder carries the antenna for a FuMo 27 radar.

German 28cm SK L/54.5 C/34 gun

German Krupp 20.3cm SK C/34 gun.

This 28cm triple turret was originally part of the main armament of the German battlecruiser *Gneisenau* (commissioned 21 May 1938). On 26 February 1942 the ship was severely damaged

German 28cm SK L/54.5 C/34 gun (see also p70).

(Aüstrastt museum battery, Ørlandet, Norway)

by British bombs in Kiel, and was subsequently transferred to Gotenhafen. All her armament was removed there, with the intention of setting the guns up for use as coastal artillery. The complete turrets 'Bruno' and 'Caesar' were transported to Norway, but the three barrels of the 'Anton' turret were installed on single C/37 BSG mountings at the Hook of Holland to form the 'Rozenburg' battery. The 'Caesar' turret shown here was set up in a gun pit which

had been blasted out on Lundahaugan near Austråstt in 1942. Designated by the Germans the 'Ørlandet Battery', the guns were ready for use with MAA 4/507 in 1943, but they never saw action. After the German surrender, the turret, complete with ammunition, was handed over to a British-Norwegian commission. A Norwegian gun crew was trained to operate the weapons, and the guns then remained in service at Trondelog as 'Agdenes Fort' with the Norwegian coastal artillery brigade until 1968. In 1990 a comprehensive restoration programme began, in order to preserve the turret as an exhibit, and it was transferred to the ownership of the Ørlandet community.

Russian Obuchov 12in L/52 MA 1907 naval guns (see also p72).
('Maxim Gorki I' armoured battery, Sebastopol, Ukraine)

The gun turrets, built by Friedrich Krupp AG at Essen in 1934, have an overall length of 21.72m. Each barrel, 15.42m long, weighs 52.2 t.

Training and elevation were electro-hydraulic. The elevation range is -8° to +40°. Various types of projectile were used, including L/4.4 high explosive shells and L/3.2 armour-piercing shells weighing 315 to 330kg. The maximum range was 42.6km.

As coastal artillery they required a crew of 10 officers and 107 other ranks.

Russian Obuchov 12in L/52 naval gun, MA 1907

The Obuchov steel works manufactured various 12in guns for Russian battleships, with calibre lengths of L/30, 35 and 40, and in 1907 the company began work on a new 12in L/52 weapon. In the same year production began of triple turrets for the new *Imperatriza Marija* class battleships and the later *Sebastopol* class. These guns were installed in various mounts in naval versions, designated MA, and also in army versions, CA. By 1916 no fewer than 126 guns had been delivered. The armoured turrets were manufactured by a number of metal factories and steelworks. In spite of the confusion caused by the Civil War, work on 29 guns in the Obuchov works – later renamed the 'Bolshevik' works – had progressed to various stages (10 to 95 per cent) by 1922. Under Soviet administration the triple turrets were assigned the type designation MK-3-12.

After various battleships had been decommissioned, individual guns and also complete armoured turrets were set up as coastal defences.

The turret shown here was originally installed on the battleship *Poltava* (after 1926, *Frunze*), but in 1952 it was set up, together with a second turret, at a site to the North of Sebastopol, where the twin turrets of the same calibre of the '30 Battery' – designated by the Germans 'Maxim Gorki armoured battery I' – had been during the Second World War. The exact calibre of the jacketed-tube barrels is 304.8mm, and their length is give as 15.85m. A single barrel weighs 50.6 t, and the complete turret 1200 t. The guns fired 470kg high explosive and 600kg armour-piercing shells, and 100kg shrapnel shells were also available. The turrets were capable of firing in any direction. The maximum range is claimed to be 44km at 40° elevation (shrapnel: 21.9km).

The two turrets are now no longer in service, but are still maintained by the Navy. It is already possible for non-Russian parties to visit the installation by prior arrangement. Museum status is possible in the future, but no decision had been made at the time of going to press.

Italian Armstrong/Ansaldo 320mm M 1936

The Italian battleship *Caio Duilio*, launched in 1913, was originally equipped with 12in (304.8mm) guns based on the Model 'T' design by the British company Armstrong-Elswick (3 x 3, 2 x 2). In 1937 the ship was comprehensively modernised. As part of the refit the jacketed-tube barrels were bored out by Ansaldo, and new liners with a calibre of 320mm L/44 were fitted. At the same time the training drives were converted from hydraulic to electrical power. The overall length of one barrel was 14.5m, and the axis spacing of the barrels was 2.28m. The triple turrets had a barbette diameter of 9.6m, the twin turrets 8.53m. Maximum elevation was increased to +30°. Firing 525kg shells, the guns were capable of a maximum range of 29.4km at 30° elevation. The picture shows the forward turrets of *Caio Duilio* after the modernisation was completed.

French 330mm/50 gun, M 1931

For the main armament of the two battleships *Dunkerque* and *Strasbourg*, launched in 1935/36, the French navy chose two quadruple superfiring turrets with 330mm guns mounted forward. The barrels were installed in effect as twins on a common cradle in the turret, which was manufactured by St. Chamond. A 40mm thick armoured bulkhead separated the two pairs of guns. The length of one barrel including breech was 17.17m. The axis spacing of barrels 1-2 and 3-4 was 1.6m, the spacing between the pairs 2.54m. Each barrel including breech weighed 70.5 t. Firing 650kg armour-piercing/high explosive shells the guns had a maximum range of 41.7km at 35° elevation, and the rate of fire was around 3 rounds per minute. The later battleships *Jean Bart* and *Richelieu* were also fitted with turrets of similar design, although with 38cm L/45 barrels. The photograph, taken on 21 September 1936, shows one of *Dunkerque*'s turrets firing.

with armour plating 180 to 360mm thick (barbettes 220 to 340mm). Slightly altered guns of this calibre were also employed as coastal guns in BSG mountings (see later section). The picture shows the forward turrets of the battleship *Bismarck* during fitting out at the Blohm & Voss dockyard in Hamburg.

American 16in triple turret with Mk 6/1 guns

The 40.6cm MK 6/1 guns were a result of a developmental process which can be traced right back to 1914, when the Mk 1/0 was first test-fired. The photograph shows a triple turret on the battleship USS *Massachusetts*. With a length of 18.69m, each barrel weighed 87.2 t. The axis spacing of the barrels is 2.97m. When the gun was fired, a braked recoil run of 1.22m occurred. The armour of the turrets is 457mm thick at the front, 241mm at the sides, 305mm at the rear and 184mm on the roof. Inside the turret the three barrels are also protected by two fore-and-aft armoured bulkheads. The weapons fired shells weighing 1225kg (propellant charge 245kg NC), for a maximum range of 33.7km with a muzzle velocity of 701 m/s. More than 120 guns of the Mk 6 version alone were produced.

The same guns were also installed on other ships, including the battleships *North Carolina*, *Washington* and all four ships of the *South Dakota* class.

German Krupp 38cm SK L/47 C/34

In 1934 the Krupp company began designing new 38cm guns in C/34 turrets for the battleships *Bismarck* and *Tirpitz* and the planned 'O', 'P' and 'Q' battlecruisers; each ship was to be fitted with four twin turrets on the centreline. To cope with the high firing stresses, multi-layer jacketed-tube barrels with a horizontal sliding-block breeches were employed. Each barrel was 19.63m long overall, and weighed 111 t including breech. The elevation range was -5.5° to +30°. The diameter of the barbette was 10.0m and the axis spacing between the barrels 3.75m. Using a fore charge and a main propellant charge (212kg) L/4.6 explosive shells weighing 800kg could be fired to a maximum range of 35.5km at 30° elevation. The turrets were protected

American 16in triple turret with Mk 6/1 guns

Japanese 18.1in Type M 91 armour-piercing shell

The 45.6cm shells captured by American troops after the occupation of Japan in the Second World War were for the main armament of the Japanese battleships *Yamato* and *Musashi*. Each shell weighs 1449kg, and its associated propellant charge 327kg (cordite, maximum 6 charges).

With a muzzle velocity of 780 m/s the guns had a maximum range of 48km. The weight of a complete triple turret was 2470 t. Twenty-seven of these guns were manufactured at the Kure arsenal.

(see also p199.)

Inside the turret of an 8m range finder unit Mk 38.

(Museum ship USS *Massachusetts, Fall River, USA*)

(Navy Museum, Washington D.C., USA)

Submarine guns

French Hotchkiss 57mm submarine gun. (Copenhagen Orlogsmuseet, Denmark)

French Hotchkiss 57mm submarine gun, 1907

Well before the First World War Great Britain acquired quite a large number of these 57mm guns from the French Hotchkiss company for use by both the army and navy. The Royal Navy took delivery of a total of 163 of these weapons, of which a few were used as submarine guns (British designation 6pdr 6cwt QF Mk I).

The gun in the picture was from the British submarine *E 13*, which was stranded south-east of the Danish island of Saltholm in August 1915. The gun, barrel length of 2.48m (barrel No. 817), was manufactured in 1907. Firing 2.72kg shells, it had a maximum range of 8.6km. Hotchkiss produced a total of 3984 57mm guns in various versions.

German Krupp 8.8cm L/30 C 1914 submarine gun

This 8.8cm UBK, on a C 1916 submarine mount, was manufactured by Friedrich Krupp in Essen. It armed the German *U 51* (commissioned 1916), which was sunk by torpedoes from the British submarine *H 5* off the Weser estuary on 14 July 1916. The weapon is a modified version of the 8.8cm L/30 torpedo boat gun, for which a special submarine mount was designed. The barrel, including vertical sliding breech block, is 2610mm long. The gun fired 9.5kg high explosive shells, amongst other projectiles.

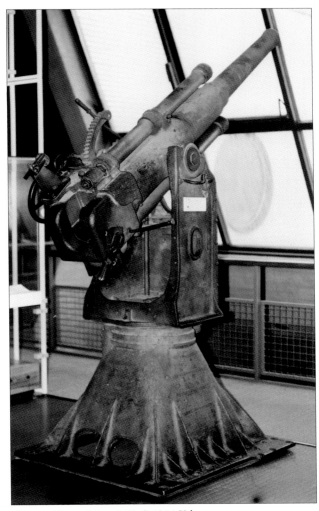

German Krupp 8.8cm L/30 C 1914 U-boat gun.
(Deutsche Schiffahrtmuseum, Bremerhaven, Germany)

German Ehrhardt Model 10.5cm L/45 Utof gun

This 10.5cm gun, displayed at the Imperial War Museum on a C/1917 submarine mount, belonged to the German *U 98* (commissioned 1917). The gun was manufactured by Rheinische Metallwaren und Maschinenfabrik of Duesseldorf, and features a solid barrel with screw breech (barrel No. 124). Firing 14kg shells, the gun's range was around 12km, and the rate of fire was 8 rounds per minute. *U 98* operated in the Mediterranean until the end of the First World War. After the armistice the boat was surrendered to Great Britain.

German Krupp 15cm L/45 C 1916 submarine gun

This 15cm gun, manufactured by Krupp, armed German cruiser submarines in the First World War. Some of the guns were acquired by Spain, where they were used in coastal batteries.

The weapon shown here formed part of the coastal batteries of Badalona. The barrel is 6.75m long, and including the breech it weighs 4025kg. The solid barrel has 48 rifling

German Krupp 15cm L/45 C 1916 U-boat gun.
(Castillo de Montjuich military museum, Barcelona, Spain)

grooves. Various types of projectile were used, including 45kg high explosive shells (charge 13kg) with a maximum range of 16km. The same 15cm L/45 guns armed the German auxiliary cruiser *Michel* (Ship 28, HSK 9, 6 x 15cm) in the Second World War.

the First World War, and used for firing warning shots to stop merchant ships and to sink them once they had been abandoned by their crews.

The gun shown in the picture was taken from a surrendered submarine after the First World War, and ended up as a trophy in Canada.

German Krupp 8.8cm L/30 C 1915 submarine gun

This 8.8cm gun was made by the Krupp AG company in Essen. It represents a development of the C/1914 model with an improved training drive system and larger recoil brake. The gun had a vertical sliding breech and a rate of fire of 12 rounds per minute. These guns were widely fitted on U-boats in

German Ehrhardt model 10.5cm L/45 Utof gun. (Imperial War Museum, London, Great Britain)

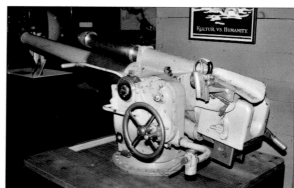

German Krupp 8.8 cm L/30 C 1915 U-boat gun.
(Canadian War Museum, Ottawa)

German 3.7cm C/30 U submarine gun

This 3.7cm single-shot weapon was developed by the Rheinmetall-Borsig AG company and produced in both single and twin mounts. As a single-barrel weapon it was also employed on various types of German U-boat (including Types VII, IX), on manually-operated C/39 submarine mounts. This was a light gun weighing only 243kg, with an overall length of 3074m. It fired 0.74kg shells to a maximum range of 8500m at 35° elevation (maximum AA ceiling 6800m). This weapon, on display in the Polish naval museum, was salvaged from a German training U-boat which was scuttled in Gdynia harbour in 1945.

German 3.7cm C/30 U submarine gun. (Gdynia naval museum, Poland)

(Murmansk regional museum, Russia)

Soviet 45mm L/45 21-K submarine gun

Built after 1933 as a dual-purpose weapon, this 45mm single-shot gun was also introduced on various classes of Soviet submarine. The gun shown here armed the submarine *M-171* (commissioned 11 December 1937) of the Northern Fleet. The weapon had a vertical sliding block breech, and had a the-oretical rate of fire of 30 rounds per minute. In the AA role a maximum ceiling of 5000m could be achieved at 85° elevation (maximum ground range 9200m). It required a three-man crew.

Soviet 45mm L/68.6 21-KM submarine gun

The model 21-KM was a development of the 21-K which appeared in about 1943, and exhibited further improvements, primarily in terms of firing performance.

With a new AA sight, lengthened barrel and improved projectile, the maximum AA ceiling was increased to 7000m (ground range 11km). However, the gun was only installed on smaller submarines and older surface vessels.

After 1943 a gradual shift was made to the newly developed 37mm automatic weapons.

Soviet 45mm L/68.6 21-KM submarine gun. (Sapun Heights museum, Sebastopol, Ukraine)

American 3in Mk 2, Mod. 2 submarine gun. (Museum submarine Lionfish, *Fall River, MA, USA)*

Soviet 76.2mm/55 34 K submarine gun

This 76.2mm gun came from the Soviet submarine *SHCH 204*, which was sunk in the Black Sea in November 1941.

Several versions of this weapon were developed after 1936 as AA guns. The submarine gun features a recoil brake above the barrel. Traverse and elevation were manually operated. Firing 11.8kg fixed ammunition (explosive charge 6.6kg) the gun had a maximum range of 13km, although the effective range was around 9km. The theoretical maximum firing rate is stated to have been 20 rounds per minute. For AA use the maximum elevation angle was 85°. A 5-man crew was required to operate the gun.

American 3in Mk 2, Mod. 2 submarine gun

This 76.2mm gun was manufactured by the Ordnance Div. Michigan, and was carried aboard the American submarine USS *Lionfish* (commissioned 1944).

Originally, this *Balao* class boat mounted a 5in (127mm) gun, but for improved air defence capability she was re-equipped with the 3in gun (elevation 85°). The weapon had a vertical sliding block breech (screw breech on some models). The technical and ballistic data of this gun are the same as those of the other Mk 2 models (see under AA guns). Above the 3in gun on the forward conning tower platform a 40mm Bofors can be seen.

Soviet 76.2mm/55 34 K submarine gun. (Sebastopol naval museum, Ukraine)

German 8.8cm SK C/35 submarine gun

The 8.8cm gun was developed by Rheinmetall after 1933, and served as the armament on German U-boats of Types VII A to VII C 41/42. Type IX and IX-D boats were also occasionally equipped with this gun. On a C/35 submarine mount it featured training drives arranged on both sides. The barrel, including vertical sliding block breech is 3990mm long (L/45). The gun fired fixed ammunition including 9kg shells of various types (high explosive, armour-piercing and illumination). The maximum range was around 12km. The complete weapon weighs 4250kg. With chances for successful use declining, a large number of these guns were removed from submarines after 1943, and were used on MFPs (artillery lighters) and also as coast defence guns.

An identical gun can also be seen on display in the Tojhus museum in Copenhagen.

Dutch Werkspoor 7.5cm submarine gun, 1939

This 7.5cm weapon, mounted on a cast bronze cradle, was installed on Dutch submarines in the 1930s. This gun (No. 152), was captured by the Germans in 1940, and bears a Kriegsmarine proofing mark.

(Koblenz Wehrtechnisch museum, Germany)

Dutch Werksspoor 7.5cm submarine cannon, 1939 (see also p196).

(Peter Tamm collection, Hamburg, Germany)

French 100mm L/40 M 1930 submarine gun.
(Gdynia naval museum, Poland)

Soviet 100mm L/51 B-24-PL submarine gun

This 100mm gun was developed in 1938, and armed the Soviet submarines of the *Iskra*, 'S' and 'K' types. In its B-24-BM version it was also fitted on older destroyers of the *Novik* class when they were modernised. The gun shown here was handed over to Poland after the Second World War. For logistical reasons it was installed on the submarine *Zbik* to replace the French gun, and also replaced a Swedish 105mm Bofors on the submarine *Sep*. The length of the barrel of the B-24 is 5.1m. Two recoil brakes and recuperators are arranged under the barrel. One round of fixed ammunition weighed 28.4kg (high explosive shell 15.8kg). The elevation range was -5° to +45°. At maximum elevation the maximum range was 21.9km. A 5-man crew was required to operate the gun, which was capable of a rate of fire of 12 rounds minute.

French 100mm L/40 M 1930 submarine gun

This 100mm gun, manufactured by Schneider, was installed on the submarine *Zbik* (commissioned 1932) which was built in France for the Polish navy.

During the Second World War the submarine was interned in Sweden, and was subsequently returned to Poland in 1945. The gun, featuring a screw breech and combined recoil brake, was also introduced on several classes of French surface warship. The submarine gun fired 13.5kg explosive shells to a maximum range of 9500m. The stated rate of fire was 10 rounds per minute. The complete weapon weighs 2.0 t.

Soviet 100mm L/51 B-24-PL submarine gun. (Gdynia naval museum, Poland)

American 5in/25 cal. Mk 17/0 submarine gun

This 127mm gun, manufactured by the Lombard Govenor Corp. in Ashland/Mass. in 1943, forms part of the armament of the submarine USS *Pampanito* (USS 383) of the *Balao* class. The Mk 17 was specially developed for submarines, from the Mk 13 AA gun of the same calibre.

The barrel of this version is only 3.17m long. With a 4.35kg NC propellant charge, the gun could fire 24.4kg shells over to a maximum range of 13,260m at 40° elevation.

American 5in/25 cal. Mk 17/0 submarine gun. (Museum submarine Pampanito, *San Francisco, USA)*

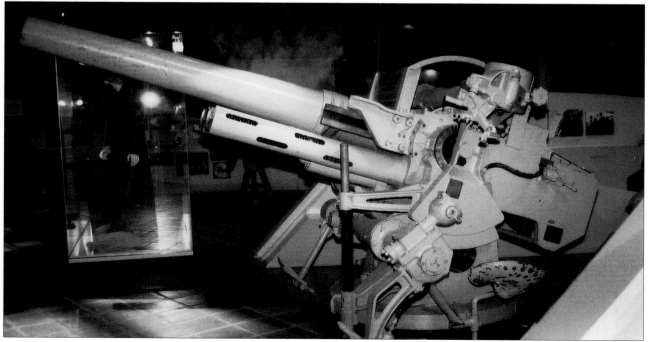

American 5in/25 cal. Mk 17/1 submarine gun. (Navy Museum, Washington D.C., USA)

American 5in/25 cal. Mk 17/1 submarine gun

This 127mm weapon is a further version of the Mk 13 AA gun designed for submarines. The first gun of this type was installed on the USS *Spadefish* in Spring 1944. Metal springs are employed as recuperators on this weapon, which features a vertical sliding block breech. The stated rate of fire was 10 rounds per minute. The shell is the same as that used for the Mk 17/0.

Light and heavy anti-aircraft guns

American Colt 0.5in AA machine gun

This water-cooled 12.7mm twin machine gun was part of the armament of the smaller types of USN warships before the Second World War. During the War a number of such weapons were supplied to the former Soviet Union by the USA as part of the lend-lease program. Here they were installed on various vessels, including the '100-ton' class of inshore minesweepers. In 1946 the Polish Navy was supplied with nine of these minesweepers, built in 1944/45, and thereby came into possession of these American weapons. The rate of fire was 800 rounds per minute.

American Maxim-Nordenfelt 1pdr Mk 6 machine cannon.
(Navy Museum, Washington D.C., USA)

American Maxim-Nordenfelt 1pdr Mk 6 machine cannon

This 3.7cm water-cooled machine cannon was the first light automatic AA gun introduced by the US Navy. The weapon was manufactured in the Washington Navy Yard in 1906, and had a rate of fire of 200 rounds per minute.

American Colt 0.5in AA machine guns. (Gdynia naval museum, Poland)

American Colt-Browning 0.5in AA machine gun

Air-cooled single and twin versions were derived from the water-cooled 12.7mm machine guns. In the US Navy they were employed for many purposes, including as armament on PT boats. The gun itself weighs only 27.7kg, with a barrel length of 1447mm. It fired belted ammunition at a rate of 800 rounds per minute. The maximum AA ceiling was 4570m. The weapon shown here is another that was transferred to the Soviet Union under the lend-lease scheme. In this case the guns were used to arm fast torpedo boats of the 'D-3' class (2 x 2). The Polish navy also acquired two boats of this type in 1946, which were also armed with a 20mm Oerlikon.

American Colt-Browning 0.5in AA machine gun. (Gdynia naval museum, Poland)

Soviet 12.7mm DshK Mod. 38 AA machine gun. (Peter Tamm collection, Hamburg, Germany)

Soviet 12.7mm DshK Mod. 38 AA machine gun

This heavy machine gun was developed by the Russian weapons designers W A Degtjarjov (1879-1949) and G S Shpagin (1897-1952), and began to be introduced into the Soviet army as early as 1939. The weapon was employed as an AA gun and also as a tank machine gun, but it was also developed in single and twin versions for use afloat. The weapon shown here was made in 1948 and belonged to the navy of the former DDR, which used such guns for air defence on minesweepers and coastal patrol boats. Shells were fed by means of belt boxes, each containing 50 rounds. The gun was aimed manually, using a front ring sight. The rate of fire was 600 rounds per minute, and the maximum range 3500m.

French Hotchkiss 13.2mm R4 SM AA machine gun. (Warsaw army museum, Poland)

was possible. These small-calibre weapons were only effective at very close range against low-level attacks.

French Hotchkiss 13.2mm R4 SM AA machine gun

This AA machine gun, developed by Hotchkiss, was produced in twin and quadruple versions. The air-cooled R4 SM (SM = submarine) type was employed for several purposes, including deck weapons on submarines. The gun pictured here arrived in Poland with the submarines *Rys* and *Zbik*, built by France for Poland in 1930. The barrel length is 1003mm, the overall length including breech 1049mm. Ammunition was fed to the gun in 15 or 30 round magazines. The elevation range was -5° to +85°. A maximum range of 6500m was possible, with a rate of fire of 450 rounds per minute. Effective range was 700-2000m.

The M30 CA version was also used in the Greek, Yugoslavian and Spanish navies.

British 0.303in Lewis machine gun

This 7.7mm machine gun, in single, twin and quadruple mounts, formed part of the armament of British light forces before and during the Second World War. The picture shows a quadruple mount installed on a British motor torpedo boat (MTB) in 1940. With four barrels a rate of fire of 950 to 1000 rounds per minute

British Lewis 0.303in machine gun.

German 2cm 38 AA gun in M 44 twin mount

The Flak 30 and 38 versions of these 2cm L/65 weapons, developed by Rheinmetall, formed the primary light AA armament on German warships in the Second World War in single, twin and quadruple mounts. Various companies were called upon to produce these guns and mounts during the war.

A special feature of the design was the ability to interchange the right and left guns in their mountings, which were offset to each other by 90°. The barrel length including breech is 2252mm (barrel length alone 1300 mm). Ammunition was fed to the gun from 20-round magazines. The twin weapons were produced both with and without shields. The guns were aimed manually. In practice the rate of fire per barrel was 240 rounds per minute, and the maximum range 4800m (AA ceiling 3700m). The left barrel of the weapon shown in the first picture was manufactured by the Rheinmetall works in Tegel in 1942, the right barrel at the Mauserwerke AG in Oberndorf; the mount was made by C. Liebknecht Maschinenfabrik in Oberlungwitz in 1944.

The second picture shows the same 2cm Flak 38 guns, but without a shield. In this case the manufacturers were as follows: barrels: Ostmark Werke, Vienna; breeches: Duerkoppwerke AG, Bielefeld; brake cylinder: Mitteldeutche Leichtmetallwerke, Harzgerode. The weapon came into Soviet hands when captured in 1944. In 1946 it was passed on to the Yugoslav navy, where it armed a patrol-boat.

(Koblenz Wehrtechnisches museum, Germany)

(Peter Tamm collection, Hamburg, Germany)

German quadruple 2cm 38 AA gun. (Gdynia naval museum, Poland)

German quadruple 2cm Flak 38

This navalised 2cm AA gun came into the possession of the Polish Navy when its four minesweepers of the *Zuarew* class were returned; the vessels had been captured after the occupation of Poland in the Second World War and were used by the Kriegsmarine as auxiliary vessels. The boats were returned in March 1946 after being re-armed. The ballistic data of the guns is the same as that of the 2cm weapons previously illustrated. Once again ammunition was fed in 20-round magazines (later also 40-round magazines). With all barrels in operation a practical firing rate of fire of 720-800 rounds per minute could be achieved. Elevation of up to +90° was possible, with a maximum AA ceiling of 3700m.

American 20mm Oerlikon Mk 2

After November 1940 these 20mm weapons were manufactured in the USA under licence from the Swiss firm of Oerlikon. The first such gun was tested in June 1941, and by the time the USA entered the war, 379 weapons had already been delivered. MK 1/0 guns were still produced to the original Swiss drawings, but all further developments up to Mk 24/5 versions were built by US manufacturers. The weapons were manufactured in single, twin and quadruple versions.

The weapon shown in this picture is one of 35 guns formerly carried on the battleship USS *Massachusetts* (dimensions and data: see twin gun).

American Oerlikon 20mm Mk 2. (Museum ship USS Massachusetts, *Fall River, USA)*

The Oerlikon gun show below is one of a number supplied to the Soviet Union by the British during the Second World War. In 1951 a number of such weapons were transferred to the East German navy, where they armed coastal patrol boats.

British 20mm Oerlikon on Mk IX mount

A version of the Oerlikon weapon manufactured in Great Britain, USA and Canada after 1940, was the free-swinging twin gun on a Mk IX mount. For a while this weapon was also fitted to the Canadian destroyer *Haida* (commissioned 1943). Ammunition was fed to the gun from two drum magazines, each holding 60 rounds. With a barrel length of 2210mm the barrel weighs just 68kg. At maximum elevation of 85° the AA ceiling was 3050m. The rate of fire from both barrels was 460-480 rounds per minute.

British Oerlikon 20mm on Mk IX mount. (Museum ship HMCS Haida, *Toronto, Canada)*

German Rheinmetall 3.7cm SK C/30.
(PK-Foto Bernsee)

German Rheinmetall 3.7cm SK C/30

These 3.7cm C/30 single-shot weapons developed by Rheinmetall saw service as AA armament in single and twin mounts on many Kriegsmarine ships. With an overall length of 3074mm, one barrel weighed 243kg. The guns fired 0.74kg explosive shells and had a muzzle velocity of 1000 m/s.

The maximum range was 8500m at 35° elevation (AA ceiling 6800m at 85°). However, with a rate of fire of only 30 rounds per minute they no longer met the requirements for effective aerial defence during the Second World War.

The picture shows a twin gun mounted on a Type 39 fleet torpedo boat, and was taken on 31 May 1943.

fixed rounds were fed to the gun in magazines. With continuous fire a theoretical firing rate of 150 to 180 rounds per minute was claimed. As an AA gun (AA sights APO-4 and ASP-37-1) the maximum ceiling was 6300m. A 5-man crew operated the gun.

Another example of the same weapon, fitted with a shield, is in the Kolobrzeg (Kolberg) military museum in Poland.

(Gdynia naval museum, Poland)

Soviet 37mm L/67.5 70 K AA gun

This 37mm AA gun, developed in 1938, was introduced gradually after 1940, and replaced earlier weapons on almost all classes of Soviet warship. The gun shown in the photograph was supplied to Poland aboard Soviet-built ships after 1945. Various vessels were fitted with these guns, amongst them submarine hunters of the *Kronstadt* class. With an elevation range of -10° to +85° the gun was a true dual-purpose weapon. The 1.5kg

Soviet 37mm W-11-M L/67.5 AA gun

The W-11 twin AA gun was developed after 1944, and was primarily installed as an AA weapon on cruisers, landing craft, coastal defence ships and minesweepers. After 1945 the weapon was further modernised, and was fitted to all warships exported to Eastern Bloc states. This automatic weapon had water-cooled barrels and could be stabilised manually around the tilt axis. The theoretical rate of fire was 180 rounds per minute per barrel. At 85° elevation the AA ceiling was 6300m (maximum horizontal range 8100m). The weapon weighs 3.15 t, and required a 6-man crew.

Italian 37mm L/54 Breda AA gun, 1935

This 37mm twin AA gun was the standard light AA weapon on almost all classes of Italian surface warship. The guns, produced by Breda in several versions up to RM 1939, have water-cooled barrels. Ammunition is fed from 6-round magazines. The gas pressure loading system allowed the operator to chose a rate of fire of 60, 90 or 120 rounds per minute. The maximum AA ceiling was 5000m (maximum horizontal range 7800m). The gun could be stabilised manually up to 10° transversely. The weapon shown in the photo was part of the AA armament of the battleship *Vittorio Veneto*.

Soviet 37mm L/67.5 W-11-M AA gun. (Sapun Heights naval museum, Sebastopol, Ukraine)

Italian Breda 37mm L/54 AA gun. (Museo Tecnico-Navale, La Spezia, Italy)

British 2pdr QF Mk VIII

This single 40mm with water-cooled barrel is one of a series of automatic AA guns developed by Armstrong and Vickers after 1920. From the outset the aim was to achieve a high volume of fire, and weapons with 4 and 8 barrels were planned. After initial testing in 1927 the first weapons were delivered in 1928, and were steadily introduced on numerous warship classes, where they became known as 'pom-poms'. Single-barrel weapons were only installed on older destroyers, frigates and light forces. The barrel of this gun, including breech, is 2936mm long.

Initially the muzzle velocity was low at 622 m/s, but this was subsequently increased to 732 m/s. The rate of fire was 115 rounds per minute. Firing 0.76kg shells the gun had a maximum range of 6220m (AA ceiling 3960m). The weapon pictured here equipped destroyers built in Great Britain for Greece. In Great Britain a total of 6691 guns of this type were manufactured, plus a further 843 in Canada.

British 2pdr QF Mk VI

The first eight-barrel 40mm 'pom-poms' were installed on the British battleship *Valiant* in 1930. Subjected to constant further development (Mk VI A), the octuple mount became a highly effective weapon for close-range defence on the larger ships of the Royal Navy (initially against torpedo aircraft, later against Kamikaze attacks). However, they were too heavy for destroyers and frigates, with the result that quadruple Mk II, Mk II P and Mk VII versions of the system were also developed (these equipped some battleships and cruisers as well). Ammunition was fed from box magazines holding 140 rounds per gun. With all eight barrels firing, a noteworthy rate of 920 rounds per minute could be achieved. The picture here shows a Mk VI weapon aboard the aircraft carrier *Illustrious*, photographed in March 1942.

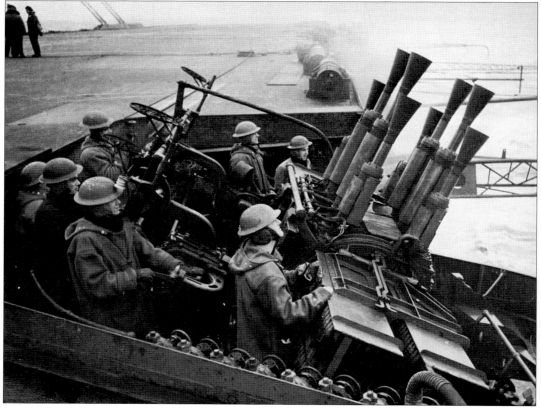

British 2pdr QF Mk VIII. (Piraeus naval museum, Greece)

British 2pdr QF Mk VI.

British Bofors 40mm Mk I

As of 1941 this single-barrel, air-cooled Bofors AA gun was supplied by British manufacturers (under licence from Bofors) to the Royal Navy. The weapon shown here was produced in 1943 and was one of four on the Canadian destroyer *Haida*. The weapon fired various projectiles, amongst them 0.89kg shells (high explosive and armour-piercing) with a muzzle velocity of 881 m/s. As AA guns they offered an ceiling of 7160m (maximum horizontal range 9830m). Ammunition was fed in 4-round clips. The gun was still aimed using a simple circular sight. By the end of the Second World War 1772 of these single-barrel weapons were in existence (plus a further 167 supplied by US manufacturers). This type of weapon was also manufactured, with slight modifications, in Canada and Australia.

British Bofors 40mm L/56 Mk IV

This 40mm twin gun was No. 4 AA weapon on the British liner *Queen Mary* during her time as troop transport in the Second World War. These weapons were initially imported for the British Army, but after 1937 they were also manufactured in Great Britain under licence. In addition to the air-cooled single AA gun, the water-cooled Mk IV twin gun went into production for the Royal Navy in 1940. By the end of the war the Navy possessed 2103 twin guns (plus 141 supplied by the USA). The rate of fire (with recoil-operated loading) was 120 rounds per minute, from 4-round clips. The weapon's AA ceiling was 7160m. The gun had electric-powered training, and required a 7-man crew.

This 40mm Bofors gun was also manufactured in Great Britain, and is now part of the armament of the cruiser HMS *Belfast*, now a museum ship in London.

British Bofors 40mm Mk I AA gun.
(Museum ship HMCS Haida, *Toronto, Canada)*

British Bofors 40mm L/56 MK IV AA gun.
(Museum and hotel ship Queen Mary, *Los Angeles, USA)*

Bofors 40mm Mk 1 gun, manufactured in America.

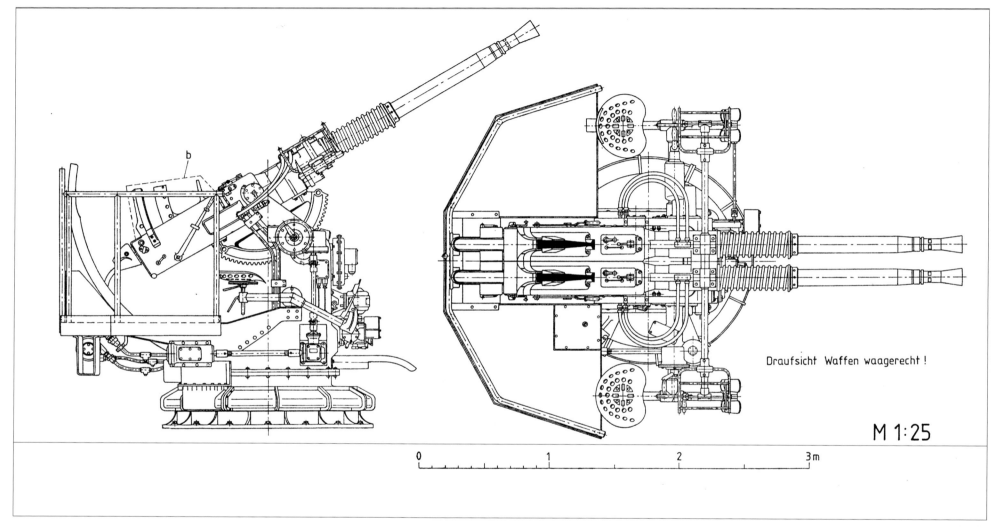

Draufsicht Waffen waagerecht !

M 1:25

0   1   2   3m

(Drawing: Juergen Eichardt)

quadruple guns (2 x twin), intended for the US Navy's larger warships. The guns shown here form part of the armament of the battleship USS *Massachusetts*. Originally the ship had no fewer than 18 quadruple guns of this type on board (72 barrels!). The technical and ballistic data of these weapons are almost identical to those of the versions produced in Great Britain.

American Bofors 40mm Mk 2

After Great Britain begun the manufacture of Bofors guns, the USA followed suit in 1941. Bofors supplied the first prototype twin gun to the USA via Finland in 1940, and in 1941 all the plans were also handed over. The first American manufacturer of 40mm guns was the York Lock and Safe Company. Initially single and twin versions were produced, followed in 1942 by

(Museum ship USS Massachusetts, *Fall River, USA)*

Russian Lender 3in AA gun, M 1915

The origins of this 76.2mm L/30.5 AA gun can be traced back to a design by W. W. Tarnovskiy, which he presented to the Putilov works in 1913. At Putilov the well-known designer F. F. Lender modified the weapon and updated it with the first semi-automatic vertical sliding block breech. By 1914 the first 12 examples had been produced, and by 1916 there followed the first 20 weapons installed in centre pivot mounts, intended for shipborne use. Additional versions designed for vehicle mounting and static emplacements were also manufactured.

Russian 3in M Lender AA gun. (St. Petersburg artillery museum, Russia)

Italian Ansaldo 65mm L/64 M 1940 AA gun.
(Museo Tecnico-Navale, La Spezia, Italy)

In 1916 the USA, Great Britain and France procured the patent rights for certain individual components of the design (amongst them the breech). In 1922, under the Soviets, the Putilov works was assigned Works No. 8 and the name 'Kalinin' (works index 'K-8'). The weapon, shown here on a centre pivot mount, was manufactured in 1915. The elevation range was further increased from +65° to +75°.

When the gun was initially used as an AA weapon, the only projectiles were 6.5kg shrapnel shells containing 30 submunitions each weighing 85g, achieving a ceiling of 5800m. At a later stage explosive shells with improved propellant charges were developed. The theoretical rate of fire was 25 rounds per minute. In 1916, in addition to the Lender gun, the St Petersburg metal works also began producing French Canet 75mm AA guns.

Italian Ansaldo 65mm L/64 AA gun, M 1940

The photograph shows one of the twelve 65mm AA guns intended for installation on the Italian aircraft carrier *Aquila* (ex *Roma*), which was not completed before the Italian surrender in 1943.

Since neither the calibre nor rate of fire (1 round every 3 seconds) were sufficient to meet current requirements, production of these guns was halted in 1943. Originally the guns featured an electrically controlled, semi-automatic loading process and were equipped with a vertical sliding block breech, but this design never made it into full production. The effective range with 4.08kg explosive shells was 7500m.

German Krupp 8.8cm L/45 anti-balloon gun.

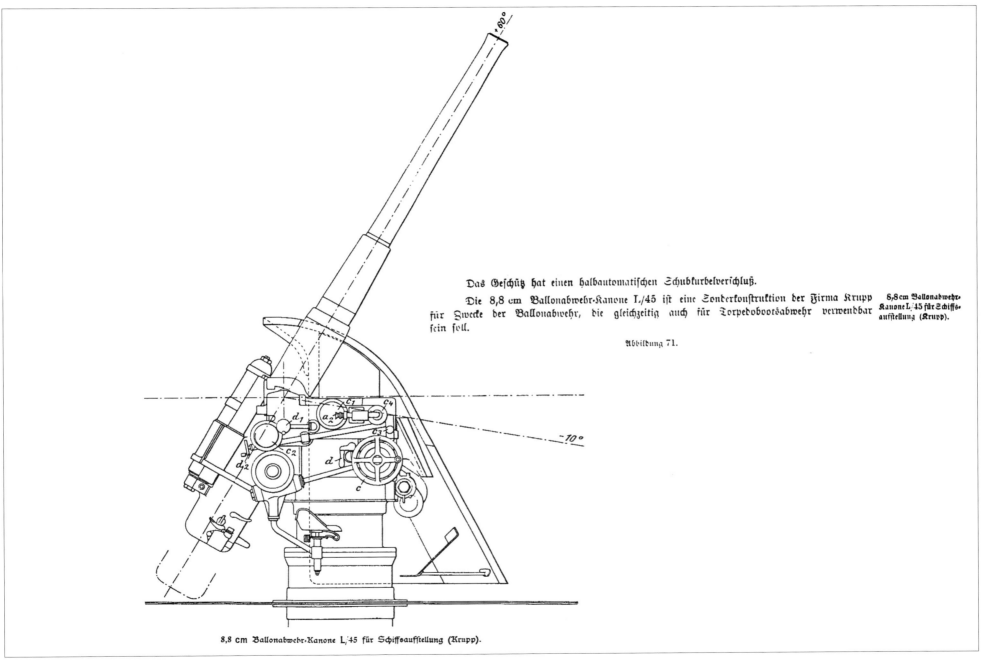

Das Geschütz hat einen halbautomatischen Schubkurbelverschluß.

Die 8,8 cm Ballonabwehr-Kanone L./45 ist eine Sonderkonstruktion der Firma Krupp für Zwecke der Ballonabwehr, die gleichzeitig auch für Torpedobootsabwehr verwendbar sein soll.

Abbildung 71.

8,8 cm Ballonabwehr-Kanone L./45 für Schiffs-aufstellung (Krupp).

8,8 cm Ballonabwehr-Kanone L./45 für Schiffsaufstellung (Krupp).

Source: Entwicklung unserer Marineartillerie 1910 bis 1912

American 3in/50 cal. Mk 2 Mod. 4

The 76.2mm AA gun is representative of the guns manufactured in large series up to the Mk 22/3, of which more than 14,000 examples had been produced by 1945.

This gun, displayed in the naval museum at Port O'Call, was built by the Hudson Motor Car Co. in 1943. This Mod. 4 gun again features a vertical sliding block breech (the Mk 2/1 and 2/2 had screw breeches). This was the standard US Navy AA gun, and it was installed on almost all classes of warship. Firing 5.9kg explosive shells the gun had a ceiling of approximately 9000m (maximum horizontal range 13,300m).

The second picture shows the same type from the left-hand side; this gun is on the battleship USS *Massachusetts*.

Photo below; see also p199.

(Port O'Call naval museum, Los Angeles, USA)

Navy were each equipped with three of these guns. Each barrel was capable of firing 5.9kg shells at a rate of 50 rounds per minute. As anti-aircraft guns their ceiling was 9500m at 85° elevation. The weight of a twin gun was 15.2 t, and a nominal crew of 12 men was required.

American 3in/50 cal. Mk 33 AA gun.
(*Museum ship USS* Intrepid, *New York, USA*)

American 3in/50 cal. Mk 33 AA gun

This automatic 76.2mm twin gun is displayed aboard the US aircraft carrier *Intrepid* in New York Harbour, but it was never a part of that ship's original armament. Developed to provide effective defence against attack by dive-bombers, torpedo aircraft and (after 1944) Kamikazes, this weapon was gradually installed on many ship classes of the USN. The six *Fletcher* class destroyers loaned to the Federal German

German Rheinmetall 10.5cm C/33 AA gun.

German Rheinmetall 10.5cm C/33 AA gun

After producing its 8.8cm AA guns in C/31 and C/32 twin mounts, the Rheinmetall company developed new 10.5cm guns which eventually became standard armament on all the larger ships of the Kriegsmarine, initially in C/31 twin mounts, then in further improved form as C/37 and 38. The jacketed-tube barrels were 6840mm long, and the axis spacing of the barrels was 680mm. These weapons had an elevation range of -8° to +80°, and training was electro-hydraulically operated. The double mount could be stabilised around the tilt axis up to 17°. Firing 15.1kg explosive fragmentation shells their ceiling was 12.5km at 80° (maximum horizontal range 17.7km). The firing rate with fixed ammunition was 15 rounds per minute, and one complete twin weapon weighed 27.8 t. The illustration shows one of the six AA guns carried by the heavy cruiser *Admiral Hipper*.

British 4.7in QF Mk III AA gun

The picture shows a 4.7in MK III AA gun during gunnery exercises aboard the aircraft carrier HMS *Courageous* in 1937.

This 120mm weapon, which also armed the British battleships *Nelson* and *Rodney*, was the heaviest British gun to fire fixed ammunition (34.5kg).

British 4.7in QF Mk III AA gun.

A special well in the deck below the gun permitted a maximum elevation of +90°. The length of the barrel including breech was 5003mm (barrel weight 3.13 t). With 22.6kg explosive shells the maximum AA ceiling was 9.75km at 90° (maximum normal range 14.7km at 45°). The maximum rate of fire was about 12 rounds per minute.

American 5in/38 cal. Mk 24/11

This open-mount 127mm weapon with an elevation range of -10° to +85° was installed as a dual-purpose gun on the *Essex* class aircraft carrier USS *Intrepid* (launched 1943).

The gun, fitted on the starboard side, featured electro-hydraulic training and rammers.

Ammunition was fixed rounds with a propellant charge of 6.01kg NC (shell 24.9kg). The barrel is 4.82m long.

On the left-hand side of the platform can be seen the four mechanical fuse-setters which rotated with the mount.

American 5in/38 cal. Mk 24/11 gun. (Museum ship USS Intrepid, *New York, USA)*

Modern dual-purpose guns since 1945

Soviet 14.5mm 2-M-7 AA machine gun

This 14.5mm gun is a navalised version of the weapons used for air defence by the Soviet army in twin and quadruple mounts.

The naval version is the only one in which the barrels are arranged one above the other. These weapons were designed for full-automatic fire only, and they were aimed manually. Ammunition was fed from box magazines, each containing 100 belted rounds.

The rate of fire was 550 to 600 rounds per minute, and it provided effective air defence up to a range of 2000m. The weapon shown here was installed on minesweepers and patrol boats of the navy of the former DDR. The gun was operated by a 2-man crew.

German Rheinmetall 20mm L/85 Mk 20 gun

This 20mm cannon was developed by Rheinmetall towards the end of the 1960s, and in its initial version was employed as armament on German *Barbe* class landing craft. The guns underwent further development, and later models were also installed on the Type 122 and 123 frigates – some being fitted on existing ships. As a close-range defensive gun the barrel has a maximum elevation of +85°, and rates of fire of 600 or 1000 rounds per minute could be selected. Designed to minimise recoil forces, an effective muzzle brake was fitted, which eliminated the need for the barrel to recoil (gas pressure loader with expanding shoe breech).

The gun featured two magazines, allowing the operator to select explosive, incendiary or armour-piercing shells. The weapon features hydraulic training and an electro-mechanical director, and the stated maximum range is 7000m, although the effective range is considered to be 1000 to 2000m (self-destruct limit for explosive shells is 2700m).

(Bundeswehr museum of military history, Dresden, Germany [formerly the DDR army museum].)

German Rheinmetall 20mm L/85 Mk 20 gun.

incendiary) with a muzzle velocity of 900 m/s, the maximum range was 7500m (effective AA ceiling 2800m at 85°). An on-mount optical sight was used for aiming. The gun was fired by a foot pedal for both single-shot and fully-automatic fire.

Soviet twin 23mm ZU-23 gun. (Peter Tamm collection, Hamburg, Germany)

Soviet twin 23mm ZU-23

This gun is also a navalised version of an army weapon. The example depicted here formed part of the armament of a *Libelle* class torpedo boat of the navy of the former DDR. For use as a ship's weapon it was fitted on a rotating mount and with a GRP spray shield. With both barrels firing, the practical rate of fire was 2000 rounds per minute. Ammunition was fed from box magazines, each containing 50 belted rounds. The maximum AA ceiling was 1500m at 90° elevation (maximum normal range 2500m).

Soviet 25mm L/80 2-M-3 110 dual-purpose gun

This twin 25mm gun, with barrels arranged one above the other, came into service from 1954. The weapons were manufactured in large numbers, and became the standard gun in all fleets of the former Eastern Bloc states. China also manufactured this weapon under licence. The gun was fitted with a 4mm shield and could be aimed either electro-hydraulically or manually.

Ammunition feed was from box magazines, each containing 65 belted rounds. Firing 0.67kg shells (fragmentation, high explosive, armour-piercing,

Soviet 25mm L/80 2-M-3 110 dual-purpose gun. (Peter Tamm collection, Hamburg, Germany)

Soviet 30mm L/60 AK-230 cannon

This twin automatic gun was developed by the Soviets after 1962, and is still in use to this day on ships of the former Eastern Bloc states, as well as in the fleets of several developing countries. The revolving liquid-cooled barrels are loaded via an electrically-driven rotating 4-round breech. The gun is fired electrically. The barrel including breech is 2140mm long. The gun fires belted ammunition, from a 1000-round magazine. With a rate of fire of 1050 rounds per minute, maximum range is 6800m and the AA ceiling is 4800m at 87° elevation.

The weapon is aimed using an MP-104 radar fire direction system or a 'Golonka' optical director with electro-hydraulic remote control. The complete turret weighs 2.23 t.

Soviet 30mm L/60 AK-230 cannon.
(Museum ship Mala, *Kolbrzeg, Poland)*

Italian Breda 20mm AA gun

After 1945 great efforts were made in Italy to improve the effectiveness of close-range AA defence by increasing volume of fire. This is shown in the manufacturer's picture of a 6-barrelled 20mm AA mount by Breda, although the weapon never entered service. Technical and ballistic data are not known.

Italian Breda 20mm AA gun.

Soviet 30mm AK-230 automatic turret.

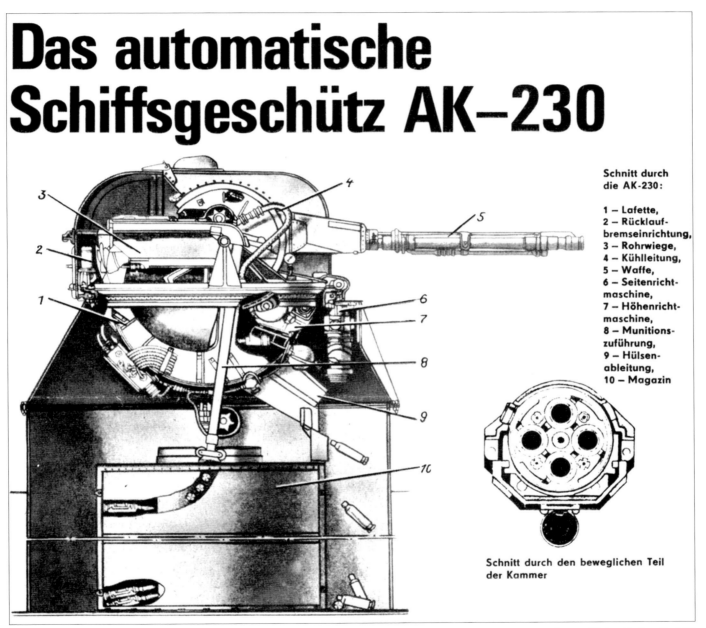

Das automatische Schiffsgeschütz AK–230

Schnitt durch
die AK-230:

1 – Lafette,
2 – Rücklauf-
   bremseinrichtung,
3 – Rohrwiege,
4 – Kühlleitung,
5 – Waffe,
6 – Seitenricht-
   maschine,
7 – Höhenricht-
   maschine,
8 – Munitions-
   zuführung,
9 – Hülsen-
   ableitung,
10 – Magazin

Schnitt durch den beweglichen Teil
der Kammer

Source: Wojennije Snanija 3/88

Soviet 30mm L/54 AK-630 weapons system

This 6-barrelled automatic turret was introduced after 1976 for close-range defence on Soviet warships. With an unusually high firing rate for the time of more than 4000 rounds/min. the gun was intended to be especially effective against missile attacks.

The Gatling principle is employed here, implemented as a synchronous-firing revolving barrel system with electrical drive. The group of barrels is enclosed by a jacket, and is cooled using a special fluid. Maximum range firing 0.39kg shells is 8100m.

The self-destruct limit with explosive shells is 5000m. The gun was coupled with the MR-123 fire control system. The weapon illustrated here was from one of the 'Tarantul' class missile corvettes of the navy of the former DDR.

American Phalanx 20mm Mk 15 Mod. 12 weapon system

This 6-barrelled 20mm cannon was developed by General Dynamics, and began to be introduced on ships of the US Navy in 1980, as a close-range defensive weapon.

The weapons system embraces the multi-barrelled gun, working on the Gatling principle, radar for target search and tracking, ammunition feed and power supply. The weapon is automated, automatically engaging targets it registers as a threat. Rate of fire is 3000 rounds per minute, and the effective range is stated to be 1400m. The picture shows one of the two systems aboard the cruiser USS *Vella Gulf* (CG 72, commissioned June 1992).

(Koblenz wehrtechnisch museum, Germany)

Swedish Bofors 40mm L/70 HS-99 gun.
(German naval museum, Wilhelmshaven, Germany)

Swedish Bofors 40mm L/70 HS-99 gun

This automatic weapon is part of the armament of the German minesweeper *Weilheim* of the 331 B class (formerly minesweeper 320 class, commissioned 1959).

The guns, supplied by Bofors to many of the world's fleets, fired various types of projectile, including 0.95kg shells which were fed to the gun in magazines. The effective AA ceiling was 8700m at 85° elevation. The theoretical rate of fire was 240 rounds per minute.

Soviet 45mm L/78 CM-21-SIF dual-purpose gun

These 45mm automatic guns were introduced into the Soviet fleet in 1954. In 1957 a quadruple version of the same gun followed for use on destroyers and landing ships. This relatively heavy gun – total weight 3.6 t – had a rate of fire of 160 rounds per minute. With 4.37kg rounds – shell weight 1.41kg – the gun was capable of a maximum range of 11,000m with a muzzle velocity of 1080 m/s. The AA ceiling was 6700m at 85° elevation.

The gun could be aimed electro-hydraulically or manually. The weapon illustrated here was supplied to the former DDR by the Soviet Union in 1962, and was employed as a trials weapon on a *Hai* class submarine hunter (the standard armament was the AK-230).

Soviet 45mm L/78 CM-21-SIF dual-purpose gun. (Peter Tamm collection, Hamburg, Germany)

Soviet 45mm/78 CM-20-SIF AA gun

The quadruple 45mm gun shown here is mounted on the aft superstructure of a destroyer of the 'Krupny' class. The type was designed by the MAZKB design bureau in 1957.

These recoil-operated weapons had solid barrels with a vertical sliding wedge breech. Targeting data was fed to the weapon from a FUT radar fire direction system (effective range 45km), although the gun could also be aimed optically using a WKM-45-4M AA sight. For the improved SIF-1, or SIF 68, version newly developed ammunition was used. This included a part-nitro-glycerine propellant charge, giving a muzzle velocity of 1200 m/s!. The AA ceiling was 6.7km at 85° elevation (maximum horizontal range 11 km). The rate of fire was 160 rounds per minute. The complete weapon weighed 15.6 t, and was operated by a 7-man crew.

Soviet 45-mm/78 CM-20-SIF AA gun.

Swedish Bofors 57mm L/70 dual-purpose gun

This automatic dual-purpose gun, made by Bofors, is shown here on the forecastle of the Swedish fast torpedo boat *Spica* (commissioned 1966). The weapon is coupled with an M 22 radar fire control system manufactured by Hollandse Signaalapparaten B.V. The practical rate of fire was 120 rounds per minute. At 75° elevation the gun had an AA ceiling of 9000m (maximum horizontal range 14,500m).

Swedish Bofors 57mm L/70 dual-purpose gun. (Karlskrona naval museum, Sweden)

Soviet 57mm AK-725 dual-purpose gun

After 1964 these twin automatic 57mm guns were introduced gradually onto many classes of Soviet warship, and after 1975 they were also supplied to the Eastern Bloc states which were her allies at that time. The picture shows the forward mount on the *Frosch* class landing ship *Hoyerswerda* belonging to the navy of the former DDR. The weapon, coupled with an MR 103 radar fire control system, had a rate of fire of 200 rounds per minute. The guns were fitted with a cooling jacket filled with a special fluid. They featured electro-hydraulic training, and had an elevation range of -10° to +85°. With 2.8kg fragmentation shells they were capable of a maximum range of 12.9 km (ceiling at shell self-destruct limit 6.7km). A turret weighs 3.9 t in total. This weapon system is still in use today in some fleets.

Soviet 76.2mm AK-726 dual-purpose gun

These automatic L/59 turret-mounted guns were also introduced from 1964, and were employed both as AA guns on larger vessels, and as general-purpose weapons on frigates of the 'Krivak I' and 'Koni' classes and on various classes of submarine hunters.

The weapons are controlled by an MR-105 radar fire control system with an effective range of 54km. The elevation range is -10° to +85°.

Various types of projectile can be fired, including 5.9kg explosive shells (complete round weight 12.6kg shell) at a rate of fire of 100 rounds per minute. Maximum range is claimed to be 5.7 km. The AA ceiling to the shell self-destruct limit is 11km. A complete turret weighs around 26 t, and a crew of 9 is required to man both the guns and their ammunition handling room.

Soviet 57mm AK-725 dual-purpose gun.

Soviet 76.2mm AK-726 dual-purpose gun.

Italian OTO 76mm L/62 Compact gun

The picture shows one of two guns installed on each broadside of the Italian guided missile destroyer *Ardito*. The 76.2mm 'Compact' model is a development of the type MM 1, which has been manufactured since 1962. The weapons, developed by OTO Melara in La Spezia, have now become one of the standard guns used by many NATO fleets. In the USA the weapon was manufactured under licence for the frigates of the *Oliver Hazard Perry* class (Mk 75). The lightly-built gun is recoil-operated with external barrel cooling. Ammunition feed is via a drum magazine with an automatic lift arranged under the weapon. The turret fairing consists of GRP materials. Firing 6.2kg shells – also with proximity fuses – the maximum rate of fire is 85 rounds per minute. Maximum normal range is 16.3km, maximum AA ceiling 11.8km.

Italian OTO 76mm L/62 Compact gun.

Soviet 76.2mm AK-176 deck gun.

Soviet 76.2mm AK-176 deck gun

This automatic general-purpose gun was introduced into the Soviet fleet in 1979, and it was carried on various ship types including missile corvettes, submarine chasers and hydrofoil missile boats. The gun shown here is the forward mount on the 'Tarantul' class corvette *Hans Beimler* of the navy of the former DDR. The barrel is 4.49m long, and was cooled by a special fluid. Its theoretical rate of fire was 120 rounds per minute. The elevation range is -15° to +85°. At maximum elevation the AA ceiling with explosive shells was 11km.

The weapon could be trained electrically or manually. An MR 123 radar fire control system was used for target location and fire control.

Soviet 76.2mm AK-176 deck gun. (Museum ship Hans Beimler, *Peenemünde, Germany)*

Soviet 85mm L/52 90 K dual-purpose gun

This semi-automatic 85mm gun was the bow weapon on the 'Krake' class minelayer/minesweeper *Rostock* of the navy of the former DDR.

The naval gun was derived from an army weapon, and was produced in large numbers between 1941 and 1946. It was installed as a general-purpose gun on Soviet destroyers, frigates and submarine hunters. The barrel length including breech is 4435mm (semi-automatic vertical sliding block breech). It was used to fire armour-piercing, high explosive and star shells with impact or time fuses. An AA ceiling of 10,500m was achieved at 85° elevation (maximum normal range 15,500m). Maximum rate of fire was 18 rounds per minute.

(Former memorial site, Hohe Düne, Warnemünde, Germany)

Soviet 85mm 92-K (BS-3) naval gun

This twin 85mm turret gun, developed after 1941, is based on the single-barrel 90-K gun of the same calibre. In their specialised AA form these weapons first came into use on the well-known post-war *Skory* class destroyers. With the steady increase in jet aircraft the gun's rate of fire of 18 rounds per minute was very soon rendered inadequate. For use against surface targets the gun could fire 9.2kg explosive shells, with a maximum range of 15.5km. For AA use the ceiling was 10.1km at 85° elevation. Fire control was by a MPUASO 'Sojus' system. The weapon shown here was from the Polish destroyer *Wicher (II)*.

Soviet 85mm 92-K (BS-3) gun. (Gdynia naval museum, Poland)

French 100mm L/55 Mod. 64 dual-purpose gun

This automatic deck gun was developed in the mid-1950s by various French armaments companies, and arms several ship classes of the NATO fleets. More than 60 guns were procured for the German Federal Navy alone. The liquid-cooled barrel is 5789mm long. The 23.6kg shells were fed from a 35-round drum. Maximum stated range against surface targets is 17,000m.

Against aerial targets the range is 8000m with a flight time of 16 seconds (maximum ceiling 11,000m). The weapon is aimed using a radar weapons director system, or a reserve system from the turret itself. The weight of a complete turret is 22.4 t. The gun was operated by an 8-man crew (4 in the turret, 4 in the ammunition room).

The gun shown in the picture is part of the armament of the French frigate (Aviso) *Amyot D'Inville* of the 'A 69' class.

(Photograph taken 6/1998.)

Soviet 100mm SM-5-1c dual-purpose gun

Around 1950 the Soviet MAZKB design bureau developed twin turrets mounting semi-automatic 100mm guns for the new *Sverdlov* class cruisers; each ship was to be fitted with 6 turrets, controlled either via a central 'Senit' radar fire control system, or a radar system in the turrets themselves, with an optical sight as a back-up. The elevation range was -5° to +85°.

Firing 15.6kg fragmentation shells – muzzle velocity 1000 m/s – the gun could achieve a range of 24.2km (maximum AA ceiling 17.8km). The rate of fire was 16 to 18 rounds per minute. The picture shows a gun on the cruiser *Oktjabrskaja Revoljucija* (ex *Molotovsk*, commissioned November 1954); the picture was taken at Warnemuende in 1975.

Note: the left radome with the turret fire control system antenna has been removed, and its position covered with a hatch.

British 4.5in/50 cal RP 41 Mk VI

This 114mm twin turrets are shown on the destroyer *Vampire* of the British *Daring* class, built in Australia in 1956.

These automatic guns were developed by Vickers in 1946, and were capable of a rate of fire of 25 rounds per minute. Ammunition was fed from a vertical loading drum in the barbette.

For AA use the maximum elevation was 80°. The weight of this turret is around 50 t.

British 4.5in/50 cal. RP 41 Mk VI turret gun. (Museum ship HMAS Vampire, *Sydney, Australia)*

Principal dimensions of the French 100mm Mod. 64 dual-purpose gun.

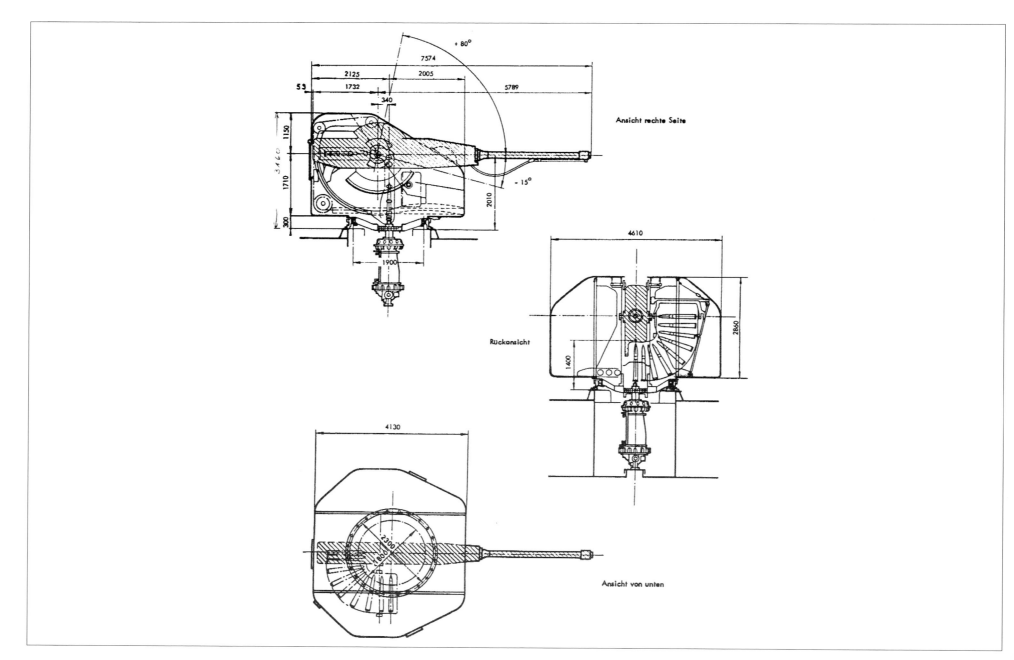

Source: Beschreibung des Geschützes

Swedish Bofors 12cm dual-purpose gun.

Italian OTO 127mm L/54 Compact dual-purpose gun

This 127mm lightweight automatic gun was developed by the Italian weapons manufacturer OTO Melara in 1969. In an effort to save weight the mount and the turret fairing are made of light alloys and GRP. The magazine below the gun holds 66 rounds. Firing 31.8kg shells the gun has a rate of fire of 45 rounds per minute. The maximum range is 23.7km (AA ceiling 14.8km at 85° elevation). The photograph shows the forward gun on the Italian guided missile destroyer *Ardito*.

Swedish Bofors 12cm dual-purpose gun, 1967

In 1960 Bofors began developing new, automatic 12cm L/46 single-barrel guns based on the 12cm weapons which they had built for the Swedish and Dutch navies in the 1950s. In an export version, these guns were also supplied to Finland and Indonesia. The turret guns, weighing 28.5 t, had cooled barrels, and had a maximum rate of fire of 80 rounds per minute. With 21kg explosive shells the gun had a maximum range of 12km (AA ceiling 8km).

The photograph shows an example on the Finnish frigate *Turunmaa* (commissioned 1968).

Italian OTO 127mm L/54 Compact dual-purpose gun.

American 5in/50 cal. Mk 42 gun

This automatic 127mm gun is one of the three origi-nally fitted to the *Forrest Sherman* class destroyer USS *Barry* (commissioned 1956).

The guns, coupled with an Mk 56 fire control sys-tem, represented a new generation of American dual-purpose weapons. For AA use the ceiling was 14.8km at 85° elevation (maximum surface range 23.7km). The maximum rate of fire was 20 rounds per minute. The barrel is 6.85m long and the complete turret weighs 65.7 t.

The two 'ears' on the turret house backup optical range-finders.

American 5in/50 cal. Mk 42 deck gun. (Museum ship USS Barry*, Washington D.C., USA)*

American 5in/54 Mk 45 gun

The Mk 45 'lightweight gun', introduced in 1974, was intended as an automatic general-purpose gun for guided missile cruisers and destroyers and the *Tarawa* class LHAs.

Since by this time aircraft could be combated more effectively by missile systems, the maximum elevation of this weapon was only +65°. The weapon features a dual loading system, feeding shells to the gun from both sides alternately.

The maximum rate of fire is 20 rounds per minute (circular magazine capacity is 20 rounds).

The maximum stated range with 31.8kg explosive shells is 23.7km (AA ceiling 14.8km/65°).

The weapon shown in the picture is on the forecastle of the guided missile cruiser USS *Vella Gulf* (CG 72), taken in June 1998.

Turkish MEKO class frigates were also equipped with this model.

American 5in/54 Mk 45 deck gun (see also p195).

Soviet 130mm L/50 B-2 LM Mod. 41 turret gun. (Gdynia naval museum, Poland)

Soviet 130mm AK-130 (A-218) dual-purpose gun.

The liquid-cooled barrels are 6990mm long. The elevation range is -12° to +80°, and the maximum rate of fire is 92 rounds per minute.

A maximum range of 23km is claimed. Since its introduction this type has been further developed into the A-192 M model.

Soviet 130mm L/50 B-2 LM Mod. 41 gun

This twin 130mm twin turret was from the Polish destroyer *Wicher* (*II*). The two destroyers – also known as the *Skory* class – were supplied to Poland by the Soviet navy in 1957/58, and each was equipped with two turrets of this type. The turret fairing was made of 8mm armour plate. The gun fired various types of projectile including 33.4kg explosive shells, and with a muzzle velocity of 870 m/s, the maximum range was 25.4km. The rate of fire was 12 rounds per minute.

Soviet 130mm AK-130 (A-218) dual-purpose gun

The development of the 130mm A-217 automatic gun for the Soviet fleet began as early as November 1967. After development and testing of individual elements, prototype weapons were built in the 'Barrikady' works. Starting in 1979 the first guns were installed on the new guided missile destroyer *Sovremennyi* at the Zdanov dockyard in Leningrad. As well as the 17 ships of this class, the guns were also installed on the cruisers of the

Admiral Ushakov class (Project 1144). The guns were produced in series in the 'Jurgmashsavod' works at Jurga (works no. SIF-94). A twin turret weighed around 90 t, and the gun fired 22.3kg shells suitable for both surface targets and AA use with a muzzle velocity of 850 m/s.

American 5in/38 cal. Mk 38 twin turret. (Museum ship USS Salem*, Quincy, USA)*

American 5in/38 cal. Mk 38 twin turret

This 127mm turret is one of the six twin turrets on the *Des Moines* class heavy cruiser USS *Salem* (commissioned 1949). These turrets were built in large numbers in no fewer than 133 versions, arming 25 US Navy ship classes. The turret mounted on battleships and cruisers weighed around 76 t. The barrels were 4.82m long and weighed 1.81 t, and featured an axis spacing of 2.13m (barrel recoil 38cm). The elevation range was -15° to +85°. With a muzzle velocity of 792 m/s the maximum range with 24.9kg shells was 16.6km, and the rate of fire was 20 rounds per minute. A Mk 37 fire control system was provided for use with these weapons.

Soviet 130mm AK-130 dual-purpose gun.

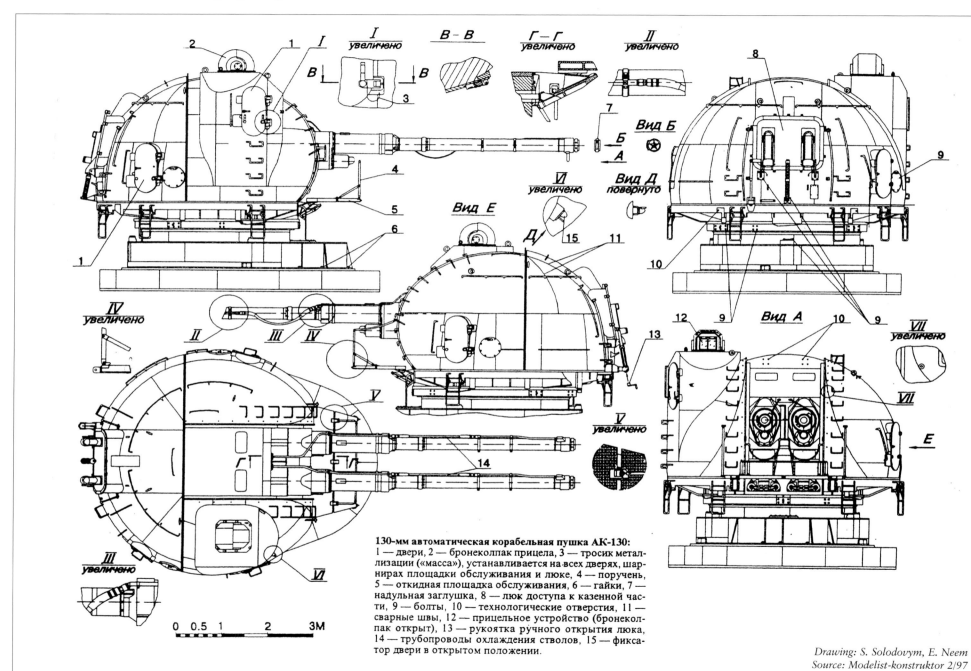

130-мм автоматическая корабельная пушка АК-130:
1 — двери, 2 — бронеколпак прицела, 3 — тросик металлизации («масса»), устанавливается на всех дверях, шарнирах площадки обслуживания и люке, 4 — поручень, 5 — откидная площадка обслуживания, 6 — гайки, 7 — надульная заглушка, 8 — люк доступа к казенной части, 9 — болты, 10 — технологические отверстия, 11 — сварные швы, 12 — прицельное устройство (бронеколпак открыт), 13 — рукоятка ручного открытия люка, 14 — трубопроводы охлаждения стволов, 15 — фиксатор двери в открытом положении.

Drawing: S. Solodovym, E. Neem
Source: Modelist-konstruktor 2/97

British 6in Mk V (N5) semi-automatic guns

As early as 1942-3 Britain developed new 152mm L/50 guns to be installed on the Royal Navy's future cruisers; these were to be triple Mk XXV turrets. Construction of the ships was delayed, and the armament contracts were cancelled; the weapons project was then modified and converted into the twin turret Mk XXVI, intended for the cruisers *Tiger* and *Blake*, which were launched in October and December 1945 respectively. However, these ships were also laid up in July 1946. Independently of these developments, two experimental guns were completed by 1949 and were installed on the cruiser *Cumberland* for trials. The light cruisers *Tiger*, *Blake* and *Lion*, which were eventually completed in 1959 to a modified specification, were each fitted with two twin turrets. Loading involved a cartridge lift inside the turret (circular 21-round magazine), two separate lifts for armour-piercing or explosive shells, and hydraulic rammers. The elevation range was -5° to +80°. A maximum range of around 16km was obtained firing 58.8kg

British 6in QF Mk V (N5) gun.

shells, at a rate of 20 rounds per minute. The photograph shows the forward turret of HMS *Tiger*, taken at Antwerp in 1962.

Note: in front of the turret is a temporary frame for unloading ammunition and cleaning the barrels.

Soviet 152mm Mk-5 triple turret

Beginning in 1948 the former Soviet Union developed new 152.4mm guns for the planned cruisers of the *Sverdlov* class (Project 68). A 'Molnija AZ-68 K' optical range-finder was provided for fire control of the initial version, but after 1950 the improved 'Mk-5 bis' turrets, in 'B' and 'X' locations, were fitted with their own radar fire control system for each pair of turrets. The front turret armour was 175mm thick, the sides 65mm, and the roof 75mm. The axis spacing of the barrels was 1450 mm. The guns' maximum range with 55kg shells (various types) was 31km at 45° elevation. A rate of fire of 7.5 rounds per minute per barrel was claimed.

Soviet 152mm Mk-5 triple turret.

American 8in Mk 16/0 gun

These 20.3cm L/55 guns are the after triple turret of the heavy cruiser USS *Salem* (CA-139, commissioned 1949), and were the world's first automatic 20.3cm weapons. The rate of fire was 20 rounds per minute per barrel (theoretical salvo rate with 9 barrels firing was 180 rounds per minute!). With a length of 11.17m – 14.9m including breech – one barrel weighs 16.9 t. The guns fired 152kg shells, to a range of 27.4km at 41° elevation. An Mk 54 with Mk 13 radar system constituted the fire control equipment. All training and ramming operations were electro-hydraulically operated. The barbette contained two revolving shell magazines, based on a system developed by Skoda. Empty charge cases were ejected forward below the barrels.

The Mk-5 turret weighed 244 t, and required. a crew of 60. The photograph on p159 shows details of the 'Mk-5 bis' turret including radome for the fire control system on the cruiser *Oktjabrskaja Revoljucija* after the ship was modernised.

The photograph above shows an overall view of the guns (12 x 152mm, 12 x 100mm, 16 x 37 mm) of the cruiser *Sverdlov* as the vessel entered Warnemünde on 6 October 1965.

American 8in Mk 16/0 gun. (Museum ship USS Salem, *Quincy, USA)*

II. Coast defence guns

Smooth-bore and rifled muzzle-loaders up to *c*1880

British 12pdr muzzle-loader, 1758

The gun was set up in the Alameda Garden close to the Trafalgar cemetery on Gibraltar as a memorial to all those fallen on land and sea. The bronze barrel is in a remarkable state of preservation, and was cast by W. Bowen in 1758 to the Armstrong pattern. The reinforce displays the English royal coat of arms, in this case that of George II. The carriage is a simplified reconstruction of the original. The weapon was also used as a coastal gun, and its calibre is 119mm. The length of the barrel is 1977mm, plus 148mm for cascabel and pommel.

Danish 12pdr fortress gun, 1766

This 12pdr bronze muzzle-loader on an 1800 fortress carriage was cast in the Friedricks Waerk Copenhagen in 1766. The rear part of the barrel bears an elegantly crafted portrait of the Danish-Norwegian King Christian VII. The script around the portrait reads: CHRISTIANVS SEPTIMVS REX DAN & NOR (Christian VII, King of Denmark and Norway). The

British 12pdr muzzle-loader. (Almeda Garden, Gibraltar)

barrel features cast-in elephant-shaped handles, and is one of a large series of 12pdr and 24pdr cannon which were procured for the Danish army. Mounted in a special fortress carriage on four large wheels (for rapid movement) the gun stands on one of the southern ramparts of the Akershus fort, commanding Oslo harbour. Between 1757 and 1815 the armament of the fort consisted of 41 guns and howitzers.

Danish 12pdr fortress gun (see also p194). (Akershus castle, Oslo, Norway)

British Carron 24pdr muzzle-loader.
(Cooktown memorial site, Australia)

British Carron 24pdr muzzle-loader, 1803

This cast-iron smooth-bore muzzle-loader, manufactured at the Carron Works in Scotland in 1803, was set up in Cooktown in Australia in 1855. Fearing a 'Russian invasion' during the Crimean war, the citizens of Cooktown sent a letter dated 10 April 1855 to the authorities in Brisbane, demanding guns, ammunition and a competent officer to establish harbour defences. The authorities in Brisbane responded to this request, sending one muzzle-loading cannon, three roundshot, two flintlock muskets and one officer, which still seems laughable today. The barrel is numbered 63911 with CARRON 1803 on the left-hand trunnion, while the right-hand trunnion shows the calibre – 24 P. The muzzle is of 'tulip' form, indicating that it might originally have been intended for shipborne service. One side of the muzzle and the breech ring bear a simple notch as an aid to aiming the weapon.

British Carron 24pdr muzzle-loader, 1812

Another 24pdr muzzle-loader can be found in the museum of Elizabeth Castle, south-west of the harbour entrance of St. Helier. This 14.7cm calibre cast-iron barrel was also manufactured by the Carron Iron Company in Falkirk, Scotland, this time in 1812. With a 3.6kg propellant charge a range of 2400 yards (2184m) was claimed. An early graduated scale is cut into the breech ring to aid adjustment of elevation. The gun, displayed on the remains of an original carriage, is the only part of the fort's armament surviving from the time of the Napoleonic wars.

British Carron 24pdr muzzle-loader. (Elizabeth Castle museum, St. Helier, Jersey, GB)

Dutch 15in mortar, 1748

Many coastal fortresses and other fortified sites were also armed with mortars of various calibres. This mortar was one of twelve which constituted the cargo of the Dutch merchantman *Willem De Zweijger*, which was stranded on the African coast near Cape Agulhas in a severe storm on 20 March 1863. The ship's intended voyage was from Ince in Batavia to Texel, Amsterdam. Why were 12 bronze mortars to be transported back to Holland from Batavia 60 to 100 years after their manufacture? The answer is that these weapons were no longer required for the defence of fortified trading posts – including those of the East India Company – and were to be brought home for scrap. The mortar shown here bears the Dutch lion insignia directly behind the muzzle, with the peripheral script VIGILATE DEO CONFIDENTES ('Be watchful and trust God'). On the base ring of the reduced-diameter chamber can be seen the mark of the foundry master and the year of casting: ME FECIT CORNELIS CRANS – HAGA – 1748

Dutch 15in mortar. (Peter Tamm collection, Hamburg, Germany)

('Made by Cornelis Crans – Hague – 1748'). On the central reinforce there is a handle in the form of two cast-in dolphins, set transversely. The calibre is 39cm, the internal bore length is 52cm, the overall external length 76cm. The maximum diameter was measured at 47cm. The reduced-diameter powder chamber is 25cm in diameter.

Dutch 13in mortar, 1786

This bronze mortar was also part of the cargo of the *Willem De Zweijger* mentioned above. The insignia on the rear indicate that it was the property of the East India Company of Zeeland. The inscription on the breech ring is only partially legible as ME FECIT (?) SEEST AMSTERDAM 1786 (presumably P Seest). The cast barrel of this weapon is cylindrical, but inside there is again a reduced-calibre powder chamber. The calibre of this weapon is 31cm, the external length 108cm. The external diameter is a constant 51cm. The internal diameter of the recessed powder chamber is 15cm, and its depth 36cm.

Dutch 13in mortar. (Peter Tamm collection, Hamburg, Germany)

British 13in mortar. (Fort Siloso, Sentosa island, Singapore)

British 13in mortar, 1855

This 331mm calibre cast-iron mortar was manufactured in 1855, and fired explosive shells. Mortars of the same model and calibre saw service in the siege of Sebastopol during the Crimean War. Six of these mortars are today stored at Fort Siloso on the island of Sentosa, Singapore. The bed is also of cast iron, and features four lifting bolts. In the field, these heavy mortars were usually transported on rollers and planks, or on slide frames. The barrel alone weighs around 5.1 t.

British Carron 32pdr muzzle-loader, 1811

Around 1840 additional coastal batteries were set up on the south coast of Australia, intended to protect the developing harbours from possible attack. Since substantial coastal forts did not exist at this time, the weapons were initially set up in open batteries.

From 1860 concrete gun emplacements were built at several locations. The 16cm calibre cast iron muzzle-loader shown here, mounted on a classic four-wheel carriage, was manufactured in Scotland at the Carron Works in 1811, and from 1837 was part of the Portland battery, Victoria. The barrel bears the No. 77836 and the coat of arms of King George III.

The barrel is 2970mm long and weighs 2362kg. The stated effective range is around 900m (maximum range 2700m). These guns saw no action, being fired only in training.

British Carron 32pdr muzzle-loader. (Portland battery, Victoria, Australia)

British 68pdr shell gun. (Portland battery, Victoria, Australia)

1853, the Oscarsborg fortress was also equipped with 50 of these guns, although they were on M 1847 mounts. After 1866 a number of these guns, and also some of the succeeding M 1850 L/16.5 models, were sent to England for conversion to 5.5-tommes (16.7cm) rifled muzzle-loaders on the Palliser method. The barrel of the weapon in the picture was cast in 1842, and remained a smooth-bore muzzle-loader; it is displayed on a reconstructed mount.

British 68pdr shell gun, 1861

Although rifled muzzle-loaders had already been made in Great Britain for some time, several coastal batteries in South Australia were still supplied with smooth-bore guns from existing stocks. The 21.6cm calibre weapon pictured here was cast by Low Moor in 1861, and by 1886 it was gun No. 3 of the Portland battery. The traversing timber slide carriage permitted the upper mount to recoil up an incline, being checked simply by gravity, friction and the breech tackle. The barrel is 3.30m long, and it weighs 4.82 t (95 cwt). The effective range was again given as 900m (maximum range 4570m). The gun was operated by a 10-man crew.

Swedish 7-tommes L/10.5, M 1838 shell gun (see also p68). (Vardøhus fortress, Norway)

Swedish 7-tommes L/10.5 M 1838 shell gun

In the Norwegian Vardøhus fort visitors can examine one of the 7-tommes (17.8cm) shell guns on an M 1839 mount. Around 200 of these smooth-bore muzzle-loaders were produced by the Stafsjö Bruk iron foundry (founded in 1620) from 1838. By around 1822 these barrels bore the inscription 'VB' on the right-hand trunnion. By

Swedish 5.5-tommes M 1870 shell gun. (Oscarsborg fortress, Kaholmen, Norway)

With a propellant charge of about 4kg the guns had an effective range of 3600m, and a maximum range of 5800m. The mount represents a painstaking reconstruction based on original documents. The photograph shows a gun in the restored 'Ostre strandbatteri'. Others are to be added.

Russian Butenev 36pdr muzzle-loader, 1832

This type of 36pdr muzzle-loader was installed on Russian capital ships of the Black Sea fleet, and also armed coastal forts.

The gun shown here was captured during the Crimean War after the conquest of Sebastopol in 1855, and was taken home as a trophy by Australian troops. Made in the Alexandrov works in 1832, its calibre is 18cm.

The barrel weight of around 2.9 t (177 Pud) is marked on the left-hand trunnion. The barrel is decorated with the Tsar's eagle and bears the barrel number 31593.

Swedish 5.5-tommes M 1870 shell gun

As the main fortress and casemate batteries of the Norwegian Oscarsborg fortress continued to expand and undergo modernisation, the first newly designed Finspong 7-tommes L/12 (17.8cm) smooth-bore cannon were procured in 1851. In 1859 more guns were added. Later, in 1870, 24 guns of this type were converted into rifled 5.5-tommes shell guns on the Palliser system at the Horten mechanical workshops. Their designation now read '5.5" riflet Palliserkanon L/16.5 M 1870', and their new calibre was 16.7cm. The barrel was 2.13m long and weighed 4.66 t.

Russian Butenev 36pdr muzzle-loader (see also p194). (Sydney centennial park, Australia)

Russian 3-Pud M 1833 shell gun

This 273mm calibre shell gun was manufactured in the Oloretz (today Aleksandrov) gun works in 1849. During the Crimean War of 1854/55 these weapons were still mounted on timber cheek carriages, but after 1862 these were replaced with iron fortress carriages. The cast iron barrel of this smooth-bore muzzle-loader is 3.63m long and weighs 6.48 t. It was used to fire 50kg explosive shells, fitted with time fuses. The maximum range was about 4500m.

Russian 3-Pud M 1833 shell gun. (St. Petersburg artillery museum, Russia)

American 10in Rodman coastal gun. (Fort Point, San Francisco, USA)

American Rodman 10in coastal gun, 1867

There are several period coastal guns kept at Fort Point near the Golden Gate Bridge (San Francisco, USA), amongst them the 10in smooth-bore cannon shown here, mounted on a riveted recoil carriage. This 25.4cm gun was developed by the US artillery officer Thomas J. Rodman, and the type was manufactured in large numbers from 1864. Fort Point – built as a 'Third System Fort' in 1854 – was armed with several of these weapons.

The barrel is 3.20m long and weighs around 7 t. Firing 56.3kg solid shot (propellant charge 8.1kg) the maximum range was 5150m. The gun displayed at the fort was not actually part of the original armament; it was supplied from the West Point Military Academy collection.

Barrel of a Rodman muzzle-loading cannon, converted in 1885 from 10in smooth-bore to 8in rifled.

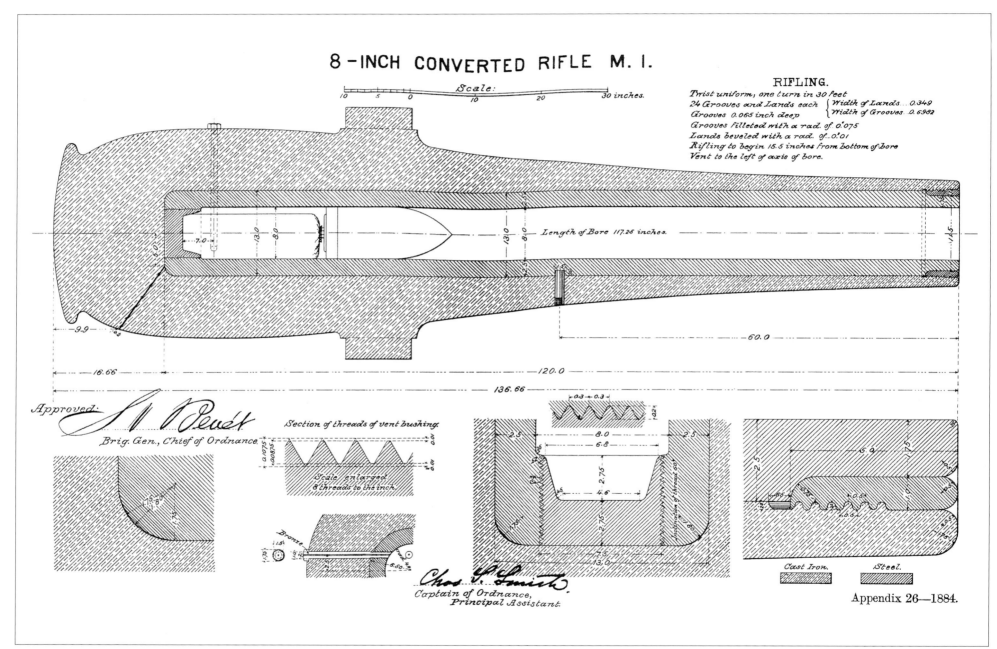

8-INCH CONVERTED RIFLE M. I.

Scale:

Length of Bore 117.25 inches.

RIFLING.

Twist uniform, one turn in 30 feet
24 Grooves and Lands each { *Width of Lands ... 0.349* }
Grooves 0.065 inch deep { *Width of Grooves .0.6902* }
Grooves filleted with a rad. of 0.075
Lands beveled with a rad. of 0.01
Rifling to begin 15.5 inches from bottom of bore
Vent to the left of axis of bore.

Approved:

Brig. Gen., Chief of Ordnance.

Section of threads of vent bushing.

Scale, enlarged
8 threads to the inch.

Captain of Ordnance,
Principal Assistant.

Cast Iron. Steel.

Appendix 26—1884.

Source: Annual Report of the Chief of Ordnance, 1884

American Rodman 8in gun, 1885

Another Rodman gun can be found in the coastal town of Santa Monica in California. The barrel was one of around 200 which were converted from 10in smooth-bore to 8in rifled muzzle-loaders starting in 1885 (barrel No. 48, mount No. 18).

With their new calibre of 20.3cm these weapons remained in service until 1903. The barrel length remained the same, but the weight was now 7.2 t.

This particular gun was not stationed in Santa Monica; it was taken from arsenal stocks and was set up here as a 'patriotic site' on 4 July 1908.

American Rodman 8in gun. (Santa Monica, CA, USA)

British Whitworth 6in rifled muzzle-loading coastal gun. (Fortalesa de Santa Cruz, Brazil)

British Whitworth 6in rifled muzzle-loading coastal gun, c1860

This well-preserved 6in Whitworth rifled muzzle-loader can be seen at Fortalesa de Santa Cruz in Brazil.

There is a peninsula on the eastern side of the entrance to Guanabara Bay which has been fortified since 1750, and between 1863 and 1871 a new fort was built containing 41 Haxo casemates, armed with a total of 121 guns of various calibres. The primary armament consisted of 7in Armstrong guns, but also included a number of 6in (15cm) Whitworths.

The large handwheel on the upper mount operated a curved rack and pinion which adjusted the angle of elevation. The inclined lower carriage is mounted on traversing trucks, and carries a second frame on top in order to raise the height of the muzzle! A breeching tackle could be used to supplement the multi-plate brake which checked the recoil.

the barrel number 873, while the carriage has the works number 438. The carriage traverses on four wheels on a semi-circular track. The recoil was slowed by means of an adjustable metal multi-plate brake. The gun was operated by a 13-man crew.

(Sea-front promenade, Williamstown, Australia)

British Armstrong 9in Mod. 1865 rifled muzzle-loading coastal gun

The two 228mm guns set up on the promenade at Williamstown, Melbourne, formed part of the armament of Fort Gellibrand on Port Phillip Bay after 1869. These rifled muzzle-loaders were manufactured at Armstrong & Co. in Newcastle in 1867. The gun bears

British Armstrong 8.5in/13.2 cal. rifled muzzle-loader, 1873

This 26.7cm rifled muzzle-loader, built by Armstrong, was part of the armament of the new Eastern battery of the Oscarsborg fortress in Oslofjord from 1874. The last of eight guns procured for this purpose was installed in 1876. As was usual at the time, the barrel and upper carriage were installed on an inclined slide mounting with integral multi-plate brake. The guns fired hard-cast shells weighing 181.2kg. With a propellant charge of 31.4kg the range was 5000m.

British Armstrong 8.5in/13.2 cal. rifled muzzle-loader.
(Oscarsborg fortress, Kaholmen, Norway)

The Veisving battery in Drobak was also equipped with approximately the same gun, although the date of its manufacture is given on the trunnion as 1866. The box frame also differs from the mountings of the Oscarsborg guns. In total this battery was equipped with one 26.7cm and three 22.6cm M 1871 guns.

(Port Feary battery, Victoria, Australia)

jacketed tube barrel (No. 17), has a calibre of 16.1cm and three rifling grooves. The barrel is 2.75m long, and weighs 4.06 t.

The stated range of the gun was 5480m. The rear of the barrel displays the insignia of Queen Victoria. The inscription 'Marshall's Iron' is on the muzzle.

The two guns, with their 10-man crews, were never fired in anger.

English 80pdr 80-cwt rifled muzzle-loading coastal gun, 1866

From 1865, fixed concrete emplacements with breastworks and ammunition bunkers were built to provide permanent coastal batteries in the south of Australia.

New 80pdr rifled muzzle-loading guns were delivered shortly after this, manufactured by the Royal Gun Factory in Woolwich in 1866.

The gun shown here stands in the coastal battery of Port Feary, Victoria. The batteries of Warrnambool and Portland were also equipped with similar weapons. The

British RGF 64pdr rifled muzzle-loading coastal gun, 1878

This gun, a smooth-bore bored out to 17cm and rifled, was part of the original armament of the British fort Siloso on the island of Sentosa off Singapore in 1880. Manufactured by the Royal Gun Factory in Woolwich in 1878, the barrel bears the No. 765. Two of these guns were installed in the western part of the fort, covering the roads of Keppel Harbour. The carriage is fitted with rear trucks to allow it to traverse. Recoil was slowed by brake blocks with clamping screws. Other forts in Singapore were also equipped with this model of gun.

In 1974 five of these cannon were found in the grounds of the Police Headquarters, and were subsequently set up in the present-day Fort Siloso museum.

British RGF 64pdr rifled muzzle-loading coastal gun. (Fort Siloso, Sentosa island, Singapore)

Russian 9in L/21 M 1867 coastal mortar

In 1904 these 229mm guns – designated coastal mortars in Russian – were part of the armament of the former Russian fort at Port Arthur. The weapons were captured by the Japanese during the Russo-Japanese war of 1904/05. However, although other guns were scrapped, the Japanese left these examples in Port Arthur in what they termed a 'Russian museum'. Soviet troops subsequently discovered them intact when they re-conquered Port Arthur in 1945. Two of these guns were transported to what was then Leningrad, where they were displayed in the artillery museum. These rifled muzzle-loaders were designed by N. W. Maijevskiy and manufactured in the Perm gun works in 1871. With a 4.8m barrel, they shot 122.8kg steel shells to a range of 6400m. The rate of fire was 1 round every 3 minutes.

Since the Japanese avoided attacking Port Arthur from the sea – it eventually fell after being besieged from the land side – these mortars were hardly ever used.

The second picture shows the same type of 9in coastal mortar as the 'Port Arthur' guns; this example can be viewed at the Finnish Suomenlinna fort off Helsinki.

These mortars, which were built in the Perm gun works in 1873, formed part of the artillery outfit of the fortified islands under Russian rule (1807 to 1917).

(St. Petersburg artillery museum, Russia)

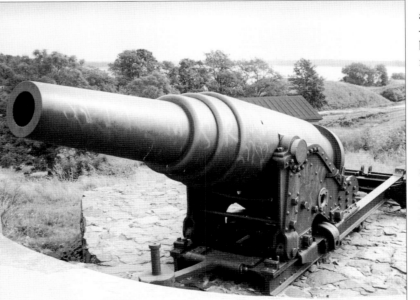

(Suomenlinna coastal artillery museum, Finland)

British Armstrong 10in rifled muzzle-loader. (Grand Parade, Gibraltar)

batteries of Gibraltar and Malta. Pairs of these gigantic guns were approved for both places, and in September 1882 they were delivered to the forts by sea. In Gibraltar one gun was installed in the newly-built Napier battery overlooking Rosia Bay, and one in the Victoria battery. These weapons, which have gone down in history as the '100 Ton Guns' – the exact weight of one barrel is 103.88 t – have barrels 7.7m long. They fired 908kg shells (up to 4 charges could be used) to an effective range of 6390m (maximum range 12,796m). Steam machinery was employed to aim and load the guns. The 35-strong crew could prepare the gun to fire in four hours. These were the first guns to employ electrical firing, helping them to achieve a firing rate of 1 round every 4 minute. In fact, none of the guns was ever called upon to prove itself in battle. The batteries were taken out of service in 1905.

British Armstrong 10in rifled muzzle-loader, 1870

This weapon, known as the '18 Ton Gun', had a calibre of 25.5cm, and was one of a total of 28 rifled muzzle-loaders of the same type which were set up in nine batteries all round Gibraltar after 1870. Made in Woolwich in 1872, the barrel is 4.35m long and bears the No. 273. It now rests in the upper section only of the carriage (with multiple-plate recoil brake) which originally belonged to it.

The gun's effective range firing 180kg shells was 4500m.

These guns were de-commissioned around the turn of the 20th century.

British Armstrong '100 Ton Gun', 1879

In 1878 William Armstrong & Co. in Woolwich began building new 17.72in (45cm) cannon for both ship and coastal use. When Italy acquired the licence to build the same weapons for its *Duilio* class battleships, the British ordered the same weapons for the coastal

The second photograph shows the same type of gun in Fort Rinella on Malta (the second gun was in Fort Tigne). At on the left of the picture the loading aperture can be seen; the gun was run in and the muzzle aligned with it while the charges and shells were loaded.

British Armstrong '100 Ton Gun'. (Napier battery museum, Gibraltar)

(Fort Rinella, Malta)

Rifled breech-loaders and QF guns up to 1910

British RGF 110pdr 82-cwt breech-loader, 1861

This rifled breech-loader on display in the 'Parade Gardens' in St. Helier, on the island of Jersey, is of the same type that armed HMS *Warrior*. The barrel is mounted on the upper carriage of a coastal mount; the traversing inclined slide is missing. The left-hand trunnion bears the designation R-G-F (for Royal Gun Factory), the manufacturer's No. 332 and the year of casting 1861. The barrel displays the intertwined insignia VR of Queen Victoria, together with the peripheral motto HONI . SOIT . QUI . MAL . Y . PENSE ('Evil to him who evil thinks'). The calibre is 17.8cm, and the barrel is 3.036m long. The screw breech, also made by the RGF, is dated 1867, and the later date indicates this breech is a replacement. In 1865, the 'Snake in the Grass' battery on Gibraltar and the batteries at Fort Henry, Kingston, Ontario were also equipped with this model of gun.

British RGF 110pdr 82-cwt breech-loader.
(St. Helier Parade Gardens, Jersey , GB)

German Krupp 15cm gun, 1880

Between 1876 and 1894 Denmark acquired new guns for its fleet and coastal defences comprising 199 Krupp guns with calibres between 8.7cm and 35.5cm. The 15cm guns – Danish designation '6-inch/15 cm 70 cntr bagladekanon' – were employed in various ways, including arming the coast defence ship *Helgoland* and the cruiser *Fyn*. The naval version of the gun was installed in a similar cheek carriage, but with riveted brackets added to the sides to take small wheels. The coastal gun shown here, as employed at Fort Trekroner and other sites, represents an early example of a gun fitted with a hydraulic recoil brake cylinder. The exact calibre is 149.1mm, and the weapon fired armour-piercing and explosive shells weighing from 31.5kg to 39kg. The rate of fire was 1 round every 3 minutes.

German Krupp 15cm gun. (Copenhagen Tøjhusmuseet, Denmark)

French Hotchkiss 65mm L/43 M coastal gun. (Oslo Forsvarsmuseet, Norway)

French Hotchkiss 65mm L/43 M 1887 coastal gun

In 1898 Norway procured several models of the French 65mm Hotchkiss gun for the purpose of setting up what were termed 'blockade and raking batteries'.

These guns were set up in many fortified positions including the coastal forts at Tønsberg, Agdenes, Odderøen and Bergen-Herlø, and were also installed on French battleships and armoured cruisers. As well as the M 1887/43, the improved M 1891 and M 1895/46.5 models were also supplied.

The barrel of the L/43 weapon weighs 580kg, and features a vertical sliding block breech. The weapon was aimed manually, with the help of a shoulder rest.

The rate of fire of these guns, known as 'hurtiskytende kanoner' (HS) in Norway, was claimed to be 10 to 12 rounds per minute.

British 5in Mk I coastal gun, 1887

This gun, based on a 127mm Whitworth barrel, was made by the Royal Carriage Depot in 1887, and stands today as a military memorial on the seafront at Cairns in Australia.

The same type of gun was mounted on British warships, but in contrast this version features a Vavasseur mount, an inclined recoil slide with hydraulic brakes, traversing on small trucks. The screw breech of this example has not survived. The massive shield is made of 33mm steel and weighs 1.14 t on its own.

The muzzle is engraved 'Whitworth steel' (barrel No. 777). The gun was part of the former coastal defences of Cairns in the Coral Sea.

British 5in Mk I coastal gun. (Cairns memorial, Australia)

American 12in/40 cal. M 1895 coastal gun

These 12in guns were manufactured in the Watervliet arsenal in 1899. They were mounted on Buffington-Crozier DC M 1901 disappearing carriages, and formed part of the artillery of Fort Mills on the island of Corregidor off Manila. On the 'topside' of the fort the three batteries 'Cheney', 'Wheeler' and 'Crockett' were deployed in open concrete emplacements. The gun shown here belonged to the 'Cheney' battery.

The 30.5cm calibre barrel is 12.8m long, and with breech weighs a total of 52.2 t. With a 150.3kg nitro-cellulose powder charge the guns could fire 481kg shells up to 11.9km.

The production cost of the complete gun was given as $90,000. Some of the guns from this period can now again be viewed thanks to the work of the Corregidor Foundation.

American 12in/40 cal. M 1895 coastal gun. (Fort Mills, Corregidor, Philippines)

American 12in M 1890 M I mortar

A special feature of American coastal defences was the mortar batteries set up in large numbers in open circular emplacements, each with four 30.5cm mortars. Beginning in 1890, a total of 400 mortars were manufactured, and the weapons were installed in forts in the USA and also overseas. The photograph shows the restored mortar installation in the 'Way' battery of Fort Mills on Corregidor. Although of limited range, these mortars rendered useful service in 1942 during the battles for the Philippines, but the Japanese captured them after they landed and forced the fort to surrender. The maximum range was 13.8km with 315kg shells at 45° elevation.

The mortars were installed on rotating mounts and could fire in any direction. The cost of one mortar was given as $23,000. Some of the mortars stationed in the USA were removed from their emplacements in 1918 and installed on railway mountings for use on the Western Front.

American 12in M 1890 M I mortar. (Fort Mills, Corregidor, Philippines)

Barrel of the American 12in M 1890 mortar.

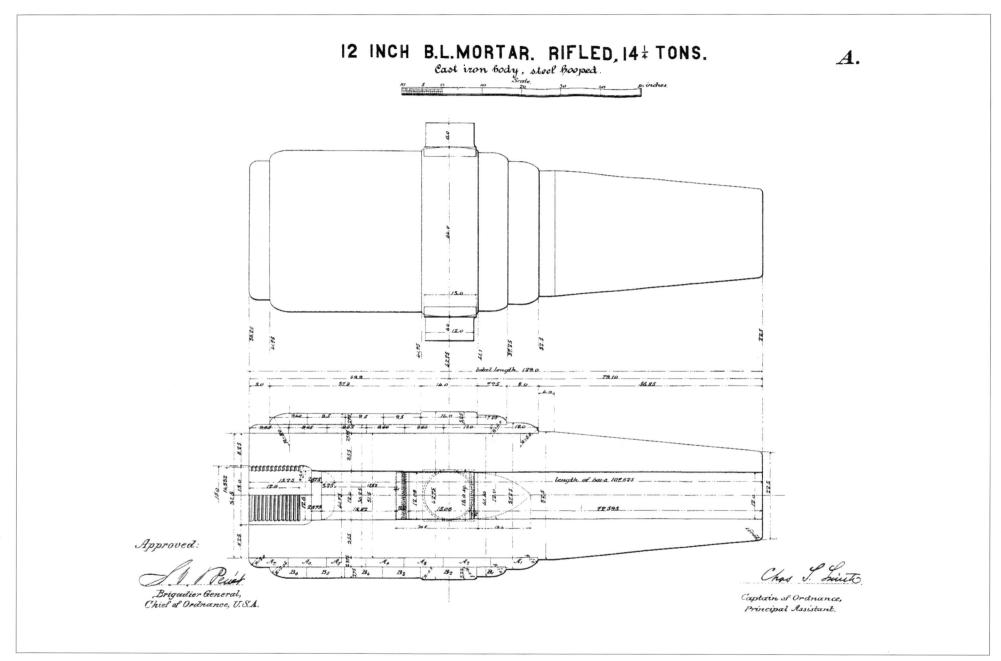

Source: *Annual Report of the Chief of Ordnance, 1889*

American 6in/50 cal. M 1900 gun

Fort Mills on Corregidor was also equipped with five 152.2mm guns on Buffington-Crozier disappearing mounts dating from the Endicott period. The guns, in the 'Morrison' and 'Ramsey' batteries on Middleside, protected the two channels on the north and south sides of the island. The barrels are 7.88m long.

Each barrel weighs 8.5 t. The guns fired 47.7kg and 49kg shells with 17.1kg nitro-cellulose propellant charges. The maximum range was 11.9km (13,077 yards). Today the 'Morrison' battery displays two damaged guns, but the 'Ramsey' battery was almost completely destroyed by bombs in 1945.

(Fort Mills, Corregidor, Philippines)

(Oscarsborg fortress, Kaholmen, Norway (see also p195))

two direct hits on the German heavy cruiser *Blücher* during Operation 'Weserübung' (the invasion of Norway), causing serious damage. The cruiser subsequently sank after two hits from a land-based torpedo battery.

German Krupp 28cm M 1891 coastal gun

This 28cm gun is part of the main battery of the Norwegian Oscarsborg fortress on the island of South Kaholmen in the Oslofjord. Three of these guns – they were named 'Moses', 'Aron' and 'Joseph' – were bought from the German company Krupp in 1892 in order to replace the fort's artillery. On 9 April 1940 the battery took its place in history when, under the command of Colonel Birger Kr. Eriksen, it scored

German Krupp 30.5cm M 1877 coastal gun

This 30.5cm gun was also part of the main battery of the Oscarsborg (position No. 4), and was the only weapon of its type procured from Germany. Only the barrel and breech were imported from Germany, the carriage being supplied complete by Armstrong. The barrel is 6.71m long, and with breech weighs around 36 t. The weight of one explosive shell was 294kg. The gun was fired regularly for practice, but was never fired in anger.

German Krupp 30.5cm L/45 coastal gun

There is a natural bay between Rio de Janeiro and Niteroi, and to protect its entrance the Portuguese and French erected open gun emplacements and forts as far back as the 16th century.

The concrete Fort Copacabana was built between 1908 and 1914, and to this day remains in an outstanding state of preservation.

Its armament comprises two 19cm twin

German Krupp 30.5cm M 1877 coastal gun. (Oscarsborg fortress, Kaholmen, Norway)

armoured turrets together with the 30.5cm twin turret shown, built by Krupp. The concrete structure contains three decks housing magazines, shell feed systems, a diesel generator and crew quarters.

The barrels are 14.52m long, and including breech weigh 47.7 t each.

Various types of projectile were fired, including 445kg shells (armour-piercing, high explosive) with a propellant charge of 142kg. The fort was operated by the army, and remained in service until 1975.

Since that time it has been carefully restored, and is now classed as a monument of national importance. It has been open as a museum since 1986.

German Krupp 30.5cm L/45 coastal gun. (Forte de Copacabana, Rio de Janeiro, Brazil)

The barrel is 4.17m long including the screw breech. The mount swivels through 360°, and provided for a braked recoil of the upper carriage. Training and loading were by hand. The guns fired armour-piercing and explosive shells weighing 275kg (propellant charge 20.2kg). Firing at a high angle they were capable of a maximum range of 7200m. The gun was operated by a crew of 15.

(Castillo de Montjuich military museum, Barcelona, Spain)

Spanish 30.5cm Mod. 1892 (O.H.S.) coastal howitzer

At the beginning of the 20th century four of these heavy 30.5cm howitzers formed part of the coastal battery of the Castillo de Montjuich in Barcelona. The guns were built by the Fabrica de Trubia, but no longer stand in their original positions.

Krupp 11in (279.3mm) coastal gun in automatic run-out mount.

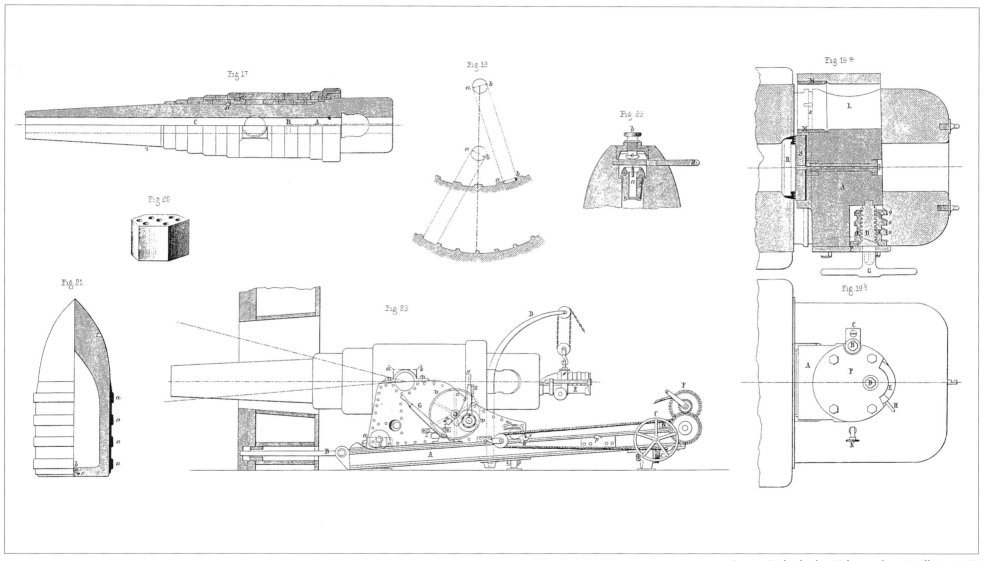

Source: Eschenbacher, Ueber moderne Artillerie , 1872

guns weighed 170 t, and were installed on inclined recoil carriages on a rotating mount. The base featured two flanged wheels which ran on circular rails (firing radius 360°). The diameter of the circular track is 15.2m. The jacketed tube barrel is 11.37m long, while the armour-piercing and explosive shells were 1.72m long and weighed around 276kg. Each gun required a 25-man crew.

(Istanbul military museum, Turkey)

German Krupp 35.5cm L/35 coastal gun, 1880

In 1885 Turkey bought seven 35.5cm cannon from Krupps in order to modernise the batteries covering the Dardanelles. Two guns of this type were set up in the 'Cimenlik' and 'Anadolu Hamidije' forts at Canakkale. Under the command of the Turkish 65th division the guns actively participated in the defence of the Dardanelles against the British in 1915. These heavy

French 240mm L/50 M 1906 coastal gun

In 1909, Bulgaria acquired two of these heavy guns for its coastal defences from the French firm of Schneider, and they were delivered to Varna by sea the same year. The guns were installed in well camouflaged emplacements on the hills near Varna. By 1910 the battery was operational, under the command of

(Varna naval museum, Bulgaria)

Captain M. Shelesov, and the guns first saw action in 1912 during the Balkan War, when the battery opened fire on the Turkish cruiser *Medjidiye* at a range of 9700m. These 44 t guns installed on pivot mounts with external loading mechanisms fired 180kg shells to a maximum range of 18.5km. The rate of fire with a 28-man crew was 1 round every 3 minutes.

Coastal guns of the First and Second World Wars

German Krupp 15cm SK L/45 C/1914

This 15cm SK gun in a C/1914 coastal centre pivot mount is now on display in Kvalvik Fort on the Norwegian island of Frei. These guns were originally used to equip several naval coastal batteries in the Arnøy (MAA 6/510), Løkhang (MAA 3/506) and Hargesund (MAA 10/504) areas, among others. Originally army coastal battery 3/976 was stationed at Kvalvik, manning four Belgian 12cm guns. The present Kvalvik gun is now a memorial, but it forms part of a series of 15cm guns developed by Krupp. As models C/1906, C/1913 to 1917 these weapons were introduced on German capital ships in various versions as secondary armament, and as deck guns on various cruisers. The guns were transported to Norway from decommissioned coastal batteries in Memel and Memel-South. The barrel, equipped with a sliding crank breech, has an overall length of 6710mm.

The exact calibre of these guns is 149.1mm, and the jacketed tube barrels have 48 rifling grooves.

The weight of one barrel including breech is 5730kg. The gun fired 45.3kg armour-piercing and explosive shells, and had maximum range of 14.5km. Later the gun was fitted with an angled breech giving an increase in maximum elevation from 22° to 30° (range increased to 19.4km). The weapon was operated by an 8-man crew.

(Kvalvik Fort, Frei island, Norway (see also p197))

French Schneider 12cm L/40 turret gun. (Fredriksten/Halden, Norway)

French Schneider 12cm L/40 turret gun, 1903

To strengthen its coastal and border defences Norway purchased six 12cm armoured turret guns from the French manufacturer Schneider in 1903. Originally set up along the Norwegian-Swedish border, some of these guns were later moved to Trøgstad Fort near Gresker for coastal defence. After the German occupation of Norway four intact guns were transported to Skudenes (2) and Midbrød (2) in 1943. The turret gun shown in the picture was manufactured in 1903. Firing 25kg explosive shells it had a range of 10km. After 1945 this gun was moved back to its original site at Halden and opened as a museum.

Russian Obuchov 130mm/50 gun (see also p195). (Suomenlinna museum island, Finland)

Russian Obuchov 130mm/50 gun, 1911

In 1912 the Obuchov steel works began manufacturing newly developed 130mm weapons to equip new ships for the Russian fleet. These weapons were installed in various mounts, and formed the secondary armament on new battleships and the main armament on cruisers, gunboats and monitors. Further examples on coastal mountings were supplied to Russian coastal batteries, including nine guns on the island of Oesel.

Some of the first guns completed were installed on the new cruisers *Svetlana*, *Admiral Butakow* and *Diana*. Between 1913 and 1917 the Obuchov works produced 471 guns of this type, and on 22 June 1941 the Soviet Navy still had 108 of them in service. The coastal gun shown here is now on display at the Finnish museum island of Suomenlinna off Helsinki.

Until 1918 the gun was part of the Russian coastal artillery system. The jacketed tube barrel with screw breech is 7019mm long, and weighs 5.29 t in total. Mod. 1911 explosive and armour-piercing shells were fired, with weights ranging from 29.2kg to 38.86kg. After 1915 American shrapnel shells were also used. The maximum range of the guns was stated to be 15,364m at 45° elevation. A whole series of former French, British, Russian and German coastal guns dating from the period 1870 to 1917 have been preserved, thanks to the initiative of Finnish artillery officers on the fortified islands off Helsinki.

The barrel bears the No. 36, is 7867mm long (L51.6) and including screw breech weighs 8.63 t. With a 15kg propellant charge the gun fired 45.4kg shells with a muzzle velocity of 900m/s to a maximum range of 20.4km at 35° elevation.

(Castillo de Montjuich military museum, Barcelona, Spain)

Spanish Vickers Carraca 15cm coastal gun, 1923

Single and twin versions of these 15cm guns were manufactured in Spain under licence from Vickers; they were intended to equip Spanish cruisers, amongst them the *Mendez Nunez* and *Navarra*. A special version was also produced for coastal defence, and was assigned the Spanish designation 'C 15.24 cm COSTA MOD. Vickers 1923'. The gun shown here was made in 1932 and was one of four which constituted the coastal battery of Castillo de Montjuich, which was built during the Spanish Civil War of 1936-9.

German 15cm SK L/55 C/28

After the Germans occupied Norway, a single army coastal battery was set up initially on the island of Senja near Skrolsvik, containing four captured French 10.5cm guns. Standard naval installations for four 15cm C/28

German 15cm SK L/55 C/28 gun (see also p198).
(Skrolsvik coastal fort museum, Norway)

guns were built in 1942, and then was operated by navy artillery division 6/511.

The weapons were a development by the Rheinmetall company, and were manufactured as single guns with armoured shields and also as twin turret guns in C/34 turrets. Various vessels were also equipped with these guns, includ-

ing the *Deutschland* class 'pocket battleships', which were fitted with eight 15cm C/28 as their secondary armament. The barrel including breech is 8200mm long.

With 45.3kg armour-piercing shells the maximum range was 23km at 40° elevation. Traverse was restricted by the fixed emplacement. All four guns have survived to this day.

The two other photographs show the 15 cm C/28 single gun with original shield, now on display at the Langelandsfort museum in Denmark.

This Danish coastal battery was set up on Langeland in 1953 with four captured German guns, one coastal radar station, a central fire control system and two AA batteries equipped with 40mm Bofors guns.

Soviet 130mm L/50 B-13-P-S M 1936 gun

This semi-automatic gun with screw breech – here equipped with a welded shield – was standard armament on Soviet Project 7 and 7U destroyers and destroyer leaders. Several of these weapons were also set up as coastal guns in open emplacements or concrete installations. The photograph shows a gun from a former coastal battery near Odessa. They fired 33.4kg armour-piercing and explosive shells to a maximum range of 25.4km. The angle of elevation was initially limited to 45°, which restricted their use as AA guns. Another 130mm battery with two guns was set up on the Sapun Heights near Sebastopol. This gun, installed today in a gunpit with blast-proof gunshield was formerly 'A' turret of a destroyer of the Black Sea fleet.

The original gun was destroyed in 1941 by a direct hit, and these guns of the same type were erected after the war as a memorial.

The detail photograph shows the interrupted screw breech of a 130mm gun from the former Soviet destroyer *Grozyaschy*.

Soviet 130mm L/50 B-13-P-S M gun. (Odessa memorial, Ukraine)

(St. Petersburg naval museum, Russia)

The 152.4mm gun had an elevation range of -8° to +47° (360° traverse). With a muzzle velocity of 900 m/s the guns could fire 50.2kg explosive and armour-piercing shells a distance of 26.6km and 22.4km respectively.

Swedish Bofors 15cm L/50 M 1932 gun. (Gdynia naval museum, Poland)

Swedish Bofors 15cm L/50 M 1932 gun

In 1935 Poland bought four 15cm guns from the Swedish Bofors company for the defence of Danzig Bay and the Hel (Hela) peninsula. They were installed on what was known as 'Hela Zipfel' in four open concrete emplacements with protective ramparts.

As 'H. Laskowski' battery (No. XXI), all the guns were ready for action at the start of the war in 1939, although only 100 rounds per gun were available at the time. On 25 and 27 September 1939 the battery exchanged fire with German warships. Three of the guns were preserved after the capitulation of Poland.

Japanese 17cm coastal gun, 1923

Two of these 17cm guns were set up as a coastal battery at Singapore after the Japanese invasion. They were then forgotten, and only re-discovered in the undergrowth in 1966 during an exercise by engineer officer cadets. The breech markings indicate that these naval weapons were converted into coastal guns in 1923, and they were manufactured by the Kure naval arsenal.

In 1976 the two guns were placed on display in Fort Siloso as a reminder of the Japanese occupation of Singapore.

Japanese 17cm coastal gun. (Fort Siloso, Singapore)

British 9.2in coastal gun. (Fort Siloso, Singapore)

British 9.2in coastal gun, 1897

The 234mm and 203mm guns now on display in Fort Siloso on the island of Sentosa were the heaviest guns used in the defence of Singapore. Developed at Woolwich in 1897, the 9.2in calibre barrel belonged to Fort Connaught in the Eastern part of the island of Sentosa. On 13 February 1942 this battery fired on Japanese troops at Etenga Airfield using fragmentation shells. After the surrender of Singapore, all the captured guns – the majority of which had been blown up – were transported to Japan, where most of them were broken up for scrap. These re-discovered barrels were presumably left on Sentosa in 1945 due to the lack of suitable lifting equipment. They were placed on display in Fort Siloso in 1974.

British-Swedish 25mm Palmcrantz-Nordenfelt machine cannon. *(Wehrtechnisch museum, Koblenz, Germany)*

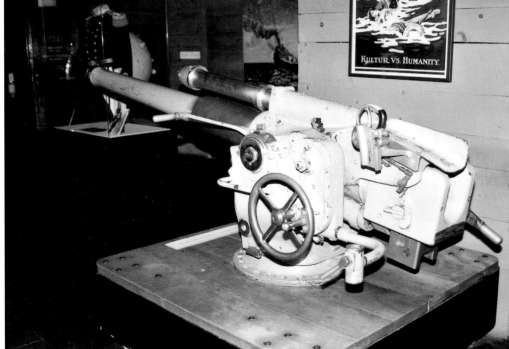

German Krupp 8.8cm L/30 C 1915 U-boat gun.

(Canadian War Museum, Ottawa)

Russian Butenev 36pdr muzzle-loader, 1832. *(Centennial Park, Sydney, Australia)*

Danish 12pdr fortress gun, 1766.
(Akershus castle and fortress, Oslo, Norway)

Russian Obuchov 130mm/50 gun, 1911.

American 5in/54 Mk 45
deck gun.

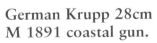

German Krupp 28cm
M 1891 coastal gun.
(Oscarsborg fortress, Kaholmen, Norway)

above:

Dutch Werksspoor 7.5cm submarine gun, 1939.

(Peter Tamm collection, Hamburg, Germany)

below:

Italian OTO 127mm Compact dual-purpose gun on the guided missile destroyer *Ardito*.

left:

German Krupp 10.5cm SK L/45 C/1901 gun

(Ankara military museum, Turkey)

German Krupp 15cm SK L/45 C/1914 Krupp gun. *(Kvalvik Fort, Frei island, Norway)*

German 15cm SK L/55 C/28 gun.
(Skrolsvik coastal fort museum, Norway)

American 4in/50 Mk 9 deck gun.
(ANZAC Park, Darwin, Australia)

American 16in triple turret with Mk 6/1 guns.

American 3in/50 cal. Mk 2 Mod. 4 AA gun.

German 40.6 cm L /56 SK C/34 gun. *(Photograph: TO-FOTO A/S, Harstad)*

American 12in/40 M 1895 A2 coastal gun. (Fort Mills, Corregidor island, Philippines)

American 14in M 1909 guns on TM M 1909

A further element in the coastal defence of Manila was the legendary 'concrete battleship', Fort Drum. The fort, named after Brigadier-General Richard C. Drum, a veteran of the Mexican-American war and the Civil War, was built between 1909 and 1918 on the rocky outcrop of El Fraile. Inside the 106.75m long concrete edifice were three levels housing ammunition magazines, fuel tanks, a generator and crew quarters. On the 'deck' stood a lattice mast, crane, drinking water tanks and two deckhouses – in addition to the gun turrets. The main armament consisted of four 14in guns, which were manufactured as army weapons at Newport News in 1910. The two gun turrets and all of the mechanical equipment were installed to naval standards. Apart from the two turrets – named 'Wilson' and 'Marshal' battery – there

American 12in/40 M 1895 A2 coastal gun

Two of these 30.5cm cannon, on swivel mounts, were also part of the equipment of Fort Mills on Corregidor. New platforms, new MC M 1917 mounts and improved ammunition eventually increased the guns' range from 12.3km to more than 27km. The barrels were 12.8m long and weighed 52.2 t. They fired 481.5kg shells (armour-piercing and explosive, propellant charges 121kg and 150kg respectively). During the Second World War these guns also took part in the defence of the Philippines against the Japanese. On 6 May 1942, after the Japanese troops landed on Corregidor, the gun crews surrendered. When American troops liberated the Philippines in 1945, most of the batteries had been virtually destroyed. Here again the Corregidor Foundation helped by providing local labour to preserve these emplacements, complete with guns, for posterity.

American 14in M 1909 guns. (Fort Drum, El Fraile island, Philippines)

were two 6in guns on each side, set one above the other in armoured casemates; these were assigned the names 'McCrea' and 'Roberts' battery. The 35.6cm calibre main guns fired 702kg armour-piercing and explosive shells to a maximum range of 21.8km at 20° elevation. All the guns of the fort took part in the battles against the Japanese, but the fort was captured on 6 May 1942. After 1945 all the moveable items were taken by scrap merchants. Today the fort is derelict.

Russian Obuchov 12in/52 M 1909 gun. (Kuivasaari island, Finland. Photograph: postcard, Vientipaino, 1992)

Russian Obuchov 12in/52 M 1909 gun

After the First World War twelve Russian 30.5cm guns were transferred from former Russian coastal forts to Finnish possession. After 1930 new armoured turrets were manufactured for them, each mounting two of these barrels, and they were set up in Makiluoto off Porkala and also on the fortified island of Kuivasaari, to protect the Finnish capital Helsinki. The picture shows the Kuivasaari turret, which was test-fired in 1935 and then officially commissioned. After the signing of the Soviet-Finnish peace treaty of 1944 the guns were removed and stored in the Hameenlinna arsenal. In 1960 the turret was re-assembled, and was re-commissioned in 1962 after a series of test-firings. The turret was finally taken out of service in the early 1970s. In 1991, however, the turret was restored to firing condition, and on 6 December 1992 a salute was fired to mark the 75th anniversary of Finland's independence.

The barrels are 15.85m long, and including breech they weigh 52 t. The 470kg armour-piercing shells measured 1.18m, and the range with these shells was 29.7km.

Firing explosive shells the guns were claimed to have a range of 42.9km. Today the turret belongs to the Finnish museum of coastal artillery.

German Krupp 38cm L/51.7 SK C/34, 1940

After the German occupation of Norway, the construction of four gun emplacements near Kristiansand began in the summer of 1941. These were to house 38cm guns, and the work was carried out by the Organisation Todt. By November 1942 the 'Movik' battery was completed and the guns test-fired; it contained three guns in C/39 mounts. At the official dedication they were assigned the name 'Vara Battery' (MAA 6/502). The gun barrels had been manufactured by the Krupp company in 1940, and they were the same models that were installed on the German battleships *Bismarck* and *Tirpitz*. The weapon pictured here is barrel No. 79. The length of the rifled section is 15,962mm, the length including breech 19,630mm.

The breech of the C/34 gun showing gas exhaust duct and pneumatic recuperator above it.

German Krupp 38cm SK L/51.7 C/34 gun.

38cm L/4.4 explosive fragmentation shells with base fuse, weight: 1031kg.
(Kristansand artillery museum, Movik, Norway)

Various types of projectile were fired, including 800kg armour-piercing shells with a maximum range of around 43km. A range of 55km was achieved with the so-called 'Siegfried shell' (500 kg). The rate of fire was 1 round per minute.

The complete turret weighs a total of 337 t. Fire control was provided by direction-finding apparatus and radar (1945: FuMo 15). After the German surrender the battery was taken over intact by Norway.

The guns were last fired in 1952, and today one turret is preserved as an exhibit.

German 40.6cm L/56 SK C/34

To protect the Norwegian ore port of Narvik during the German occupation, a number of artillery batteries were erected north and south of the West fjord, including seven heavy coastal guns. The weapons installed were 40.6cm barrels manufactured by Krupp AG. These were later known as 'Adolf guns', and had originally been intended to equip the planned 'H' class battleships. Both batteries were installed in C/34 BSG mountings, construction starting in mid-1942. The gun shown here belonged to the Northern 'Trondenes battery' in Harstad, which, as MKB 5/511, was equipped with four guns; 'Dietl' battery on Engeloga (MKB 4/516), had three guns. The complete battery was ready for action in August 1943, but by the end of the war the guns had never been fired in anger. The length of the barrel including breech is 23m, and each barrel weighs 158.7 t. The rear section and breech alone weigh 3.65 t.

The guns were designed to fire various types of projectile, including explosive, armour-piercing and so-called 'Adolf shells' (1020kg, 1030kg and 610kg respectively). The latter were special lightweight projectiles with nose or base fuses, with which a maximum range of 56km was achieved. The turrets were only lightly armoured, and they were installed in circular open concrete emplacements with a circular ammunition channel.

The rate of fire was 1 round per minute, and a crew of 68 men was required to operate the gun.

Photograph: TO-FOTOA A/S Harstad (see also p200).

Inside the turret of the 40.6cm gun. Left: part charge and cartridge, right: shells.

After the end of the war all four Trondenes guns were taken over by the Norwegian army, together with an ammunition supply of 1227 high explosive, armour-piercing and 'Adolf shells'. A German gun crew trained the Norwegians.

The last time the guns were fired was in 1957, when they were used against targets out to sea at a range of 25km.

The battery was taken out of commission in 1961, and one gun was subsequently restored as an exhibit. Today it can be viewed only by prior appointment.

Explosive L/4.8 shells with nose fuse and fairing.
(Trondenes artillery museum, Norway)

Land-based naval anti-aircraft and railway guns

German 10.5cm L/45 SK C/30 on 8.8cm C/30 centre pivot mount

The Germany Navy had procured various types of gun for static use, including the C/30 and C/32 10.5cm AA gun developed by Rheinmetall-Borsig AG. The gun shown here in a C/30 8.8cm centre pivot mount, set up in an open concrete emplacement, was manned by MFLA 716 at the Frederikshaven Nord battery.

It was to protect the 15cm guns of MKB 521 of the 1st MAA, which was also stationed there. The barrels of these weapons are 4.75m long.

Firing 15.1kg explosive shells with a muzzle velocity of 785m/s the AA ceiling was 15.3km.

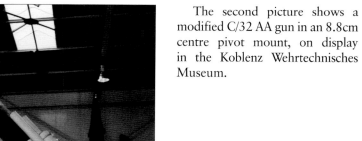

The second picture shows a modified C/32 AA gun in an 8.8cm centre pivot mount, on display in the Koblenz Wehrtechnisches Museum.

(Frederikshaven coastal museum, Denmark)

Norway – is today on display in Fort Kugelbake in Cuxhaven, as an example of the four guns of the same type which served here as a naval AA battery during the Second World War.

(Fort Kugelbake, Cuxhaven, Germany)

German 10.5cm SK C/32 on 8.8cm centre pivot mount C/30 D

A further development of the C/32 10.5 cm AA gun was the version fitted with a rotating shield to provide protection against shell splinters and naval gun-fire. The gun shown here – on permanent loan from

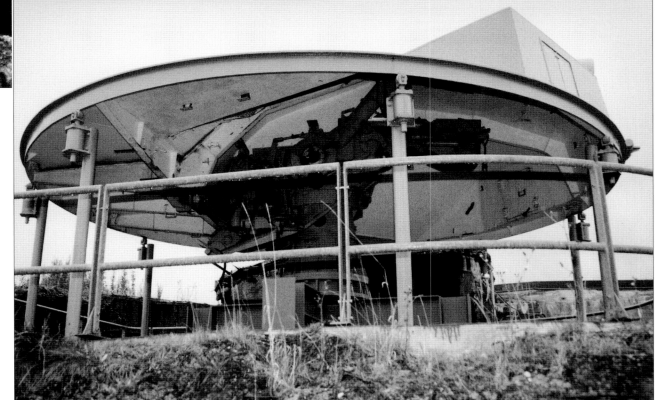

Japanese 12cm/45 naval AA gun, 1921

The Japanese established several naval AA batteries on Singapore after their invasion in 1942. The 12 cm AA gun was a version of weapons originally intended for both ship and land use, of which a total of 3000 were built. Two of these guns were re-discovered in 1979 near Uper Peirce. The breech markings indicate it was manufactured at Kure naval arsenal in 1944. For AA use the gun was capable of a ceiling of 10,000m at 75° elevation firing 20.4kg explosive shells. This entirely manually-operated gun had a rate of fire of 10 rounds per minute.

American 14in/50 cal. Mk IV naval railway gun

In November 1917, in an effort to increase the US Army's long-range heavy artillery in France, development began of five naval railway guns, which were designed and built in record time. Each gun was part of an entire battery train, which included a locomotive

Japanese 12cm/45 naval AA gun. (Fort Siloso, Singapore)

with additional tank wagons (oil fired) and a further 12 special wagons. These batteries were assigned the numbers 1 to 5. The following organisations were involved their manufacture: the Naval Gun Factory in Washington (gun barrels), the Baldwin Locomotive Works (locomotives and gun wagons) and the Standard Steel Car Co. (72 special wagons). The gun chosen was the 35.6cm naval gun, which was already in production for US battleships. The barrel was mounted in a fore-and-aft box-type bearer. The fore-and-aft bearers are supported on four bogies, each

American 14in/50 cal. Mk IV naval railway gun. (Navy Museum, Washington D.C., USA)

TM-1 gun is a modified version of the weapons installed on cruisers in single and triple turrets. With an overall length of 19.9m the gun weighs 160 t; it had to be braced in order to fire at an angle to the track. The elevation limit was +50°, the traverse 180°.

Various projectiles were available, including 98.7kg explosive shells (charge 37.5kg) which gave a range of 37.7km. It took 60 minutes to prepare the gun for firing. The gun shown here did not take part in the re-capture of the Crimea. It was set up after the war as a memorial to the naval coastal artillery in Sebastopol.

Memorial at Sebastopol railway station, Ukraine.

with three axles. At 15° elevation it was possible to fire from the railway track, but from 15° to 43° a special platform had to be built and the gun dismounted. The weapons fired 544kg explosive shells to a maximum range of 38.2km at 43° elevation. Command of all the railway batteries was assigned to Captain (later Rear-Admiral) C. P. Plunket. The equipment was shipped to the French port of St. Nazaire beginning on 20 July 1918, and the final battery (No. 5) found its way to the front on 26 September of the same year. All the batteries were in use before the Armistice, and they fired a total of 782 rounds. After the end of the war all the batteries were transported back to the USA, where they occasionally served as mobile coastal artillery.

Soviet 180mm/57 TM-1-180 naval railway gun

In 1934 development work on various railway guns began in the Soviet Union, and these weapons were generally assigned to the navy for use as mobile coastal artillery. With calibres ranging from 13.0cm to 40.6cm, all were developed from naval guns. The barrel of the

Abbreviations

AA = anti-aircraft

AK = (Rus) Artillerinyi komplex ('Gun model')

BSG (mounting) = Bettungsschiessgerüst ('Platform firing frame' similar to a railway gun mounting, but without the bogies.)

c = *circa*

cal. = calibre

cm = centimetre

cwt = hundredweight

DDR = German Democratic Republic ('East Germany')

GRP = Glass-reinforced plastic

in = inch

kg = kilogramme

km = kilometre

m = metre

MAA = (Ger) Marine Artillerieabteilung ('Naval Artillery Detachment')

MFLA = (Ger) Marine Flak-Abteilung ('Naval Anti-aircraft Detachment')

MKB = (Ger) Marineküstenbatterie ('Naval Coastal Battery')

Mk = mark

mm = milllimetre

Mod = model

m/s = metres per second

NATO = North Atlantic Treaty Organisation

NC = nitrocellulose

OTO = Odero-Terni-Orlando (Italian weapons manufacturer)

pdr = pounder (gun)

QF = quick-fire, *ie* gun firing fixed ammunition.

RGF = Royal Gun Factory

SK = (Ger) Schnellladekanone, *ie* gun firing separate ammunition with cased charges.

t = tonne

USA = United States of America

Utof = (Ger) U-Boot-, Torpedoboot und Fliegerabwehrkanone ('Submarine, Torpedo-boat and anti-aircraft gun')

Historical Weights and Measures

An explanation of units of measurement from the history of various peoples and nations – just relating to the history of shipbuilding and artillery – would fill a whole book. In spite of the introduction of the International System of Units (SI) in 1960, some traditional units of dimension and weight have survived to this day.

The table below summarises selected historical and foreign units of measurement in so far as they are relevant to artillery. They may be useful for various conversions and comparisons.

Great Britain, 1884

1 inch	=	25.399mm
1 foot = 12 inches	=	304.8mm
1 yard = 3 feet	=	914.4mm
1 mile (land)	=	1.609km
1 mile (sea)	=	1.851km
1 grain	=	0.0647g
1 dram (dr)	=	1.771g
1 ounce (oz) = 16dr	=	28.349g
1 pound (lb) = 16oz	=	0.453kg
1 quarter (qr) = 28lbs	=	12.7kg
1 cwt = 4 qrs	=	50.8kg
1 ton = 20cwt	=	1016.04kg

France *c*1793

1 ligne	=	2.31mm
1 pouce = 12 ligne	=	27.77mm
1 pied = 12 pouces	=	333.33mm
1 toise = 6 pieds	=	1.949m
1 grain	=	0.0531g
1 gros	=	3.82g
1 once = 8 gros	=	30.59g
1 marc = 8 onces	=	244.75g
1 poids de marc	=	489.50g
1 charge	=	146.85kg
1 millier	=	489.50kg

1812-1840

1 once	=	31.25g
1 quarteron = 4 onces	=	125g
1 livre (Paris)	=	552g
1 livre (Lyon)	=	380g
1 livre usuelle	=	500g

Italy 1850

1 piede	=	297.58mm
1 passo = 5 piede	=	1.48m
1 parto	=	83.02m
1 palmo = 3 parti	=	249.07m

Old weights

1 grano	=	49.16mg
1 denaro = 24 granos	=	1.18g
1 pound	=	326.29g

Metric system from 1861

1 denaro	=	1.0g
1 libra = 1000 denaros	=	1.0kg

Netherlands

Rhenish system

1 lijn	=	2.18mm
1 duim = 12 lijn	=	26.16mm
1 voet = 12 duim	=	313.94mm
1 roede = 12 voet	=	3.76m
1 pond	=	472.51g

Metric system 1820-1870

1 streep	=	1.0mm
1 duim	=	10.0mm
1 palen	=	100.0mm
1 ell	=	1.0m
1 roede	=	10.0m
1 mijl	=	1.0km
1 wigtijes	=	1.0g
1 lood	=	10.g
1 ons	=	100.0g
1 pond	=	1.0kg

Norway

(For a period, Danish or Swedish measurements were used)

1 stroo	=	2.17mm
1 duim = 12 stroo	=	26.15mm
1 voet = 12 duim	=	313.8mm
1 el = 2 voet	=	627.7mm
1 vaam = 3 el	=	1883.1mm

Old system

1 fot	=	313.7mm
1 favn = 6 fot	=	1.88m
1 mil	=	11.29km

1887

1 Tomme (Zoll)	=	0.02615m
1 Fod = 12 Zoll	=	0.313m
1 quenten	=	3.89g
1 loth = 1 quenten	=	15.56g
1 ounce = 12 loth	=	31.13g
1 pund	=	498.1g
1 lispund = 16 pund	=	7.96kg

Prussia 1816

1 Punkt	=	0.261mm
1 Linie = 10 Punkte	=	2.61mm
1 Zoll = 10 Linien	=	26.15mm
1 Fuss = 12 Zoll	=	313.8mm
1 Elle	=	666.8mm
1 Schritt	=	752.9mm
1 Ruthe = 12 Fuss	=	3.76m
1 Quentchen (Qt)	=	3.65g
1 Loth = 4 Qt	=	14.61g
1 Pfund (Pfd) = 32 Loth	=	467.7g
1 Centner = 110 Pfd	=	51.44kg

Russia 1856

1 lijn	=	2.53mm
1 djuim (Zoll)	=	25.39mm
1 voet = 12 djuim	=	304.79mm
1 archine	=	711.18mm
1 saschen	=	2.13m
1 verst = 500 saschen	=	1.066km
1 solotnik	=	4.26g
1 funt (Artillerie)	=	489.1g
1 pud = 40 funt	=	16.35kg
1 berkovetz = 10 pud	=	163.5kg

Sweden from 1878

1 tum	=	29.68mm
1 fot = 10 tums	=	296.8mm
1 alen = 2 fots	=	593.67mm
1 favn = 3 alen	=	1.78m

1 ort	=	4.25g
1 mark = 50 orts	=	212.6g
1 skal pund = 100 orts	=	425.15g
1 zentner	=	42.51kg
1 skippund	=	170.0kg

Spain

1 pulgado	=	23.19mm
1 palmo = 9 pulgados	=	208.75mm
1 pie (Castilian)	=	278.3mm
1 vara = 3 pies	=	832.3mm
1 Cable = 110.8 Brazas	=	185.25mm
1 Milla = 10 cables	=	1853.16m
1 grano	=	0.149g
1 adarma = 12 granos	=	1.79g
1 ochava = 2 adarmas	=	3.59g
1 unza	=	28.7g
1 cuarterone	=	115.0g
1 libra = 4 cuarterones	=	460.13g
1 arroba = 25 libras	=	11.50kg

French metric measurements and weights were introduced after 1859.

USA

In the USA British weights and measures were used almost exclusively for matters relating to artillery.

These tables were compiled with the kind permission of Rudolf Roth, based on his work: Linear measurements and weights. A compilation in alphabetical order of location. Published in the Quarterly Ordnance Society newsletters (extracts).

Bibliography

Aktenfolge, *Dienstvorschriften der Kaiserlichen Marine, Entwicklung unserer Marineartillerie* (Reichsmarineamt, Akten ab 1905 bis 1913)

—————, *Entwicklung unserer Marineartillerie 1913 bis 1920* (Reichswehrministerium Berlin, 1923)

Artillerie-Unterrichte für die K K Kriegsmarine (Thiel und Atlas, Pola, 1903), I

Aufheimer, A, *Schiffsbewaffnung von der Anfängen bis zur Mitte des 19. Jahrhunderts* (VEB Hinstorff Verlag Rostock, 1983)

Autorenkollektiv, *Morskaja artillerija otetshestvennogo Voenno – Morskogo Flota* (St Petersburg, 1995)

Bartsch, W H, 'Corregidor of Eternal Memory', *After the Battle* 23 (1979)

Benqt, S V, *Annual Report of the Chief of Ordnance to the Secretary of War* (Government Printing Office, Washington, 1884-1889)

Boudriot, Jean, *Artillerie de Mer France 1650-1850* (ANCRE, Paris, 1992)

Breyer, S, *Schlachtschiffe 1905-1992* (Podzun-Pallas-Verlag, Friedberg/H, 1993), Vols 1 & 2

—————, *Schlachtschiffe und Schlachtkreuzer 1905-1970* (J F Lehmanns Verlag, München, 1970)

Campbell, John, *Naval Weapons of World War Two* (Conway Maritime Press, London, 1985)

Caruana, A B, *The History of English Sea Ordnance* (Jean Boudriot Publications, Rotherfield, 1994), Vol I, 1523-1715

Denby, E, *The United States Navy Railway Batteries in France* (Government Printing Office, Washington, 1992)

De Beer, C, *The Art of Gunfounding* (Jean Boudriot Publications, Rotherfield, 1991)

Dienstvorschriften, *Beschreibung der Geschütze 25-mm 2-M-3, 14.5-mm, 37-mm W-11-M, 30-mm AK 230, 30-mm AK 630* (Kommando der Volksmarine, Rostock, 1979-1985)

Egger, M, 'Ein Besuch der amerikanischen Küstenbefestigungen von Manila', *Deutsches Atlantikwall Archiv* No. 29 (Verlag Harry Lipman, Köln, 1997)

—————, 'Ein Besuch der brasilianischen Küstenbefestigungen von Santos und Rio de Janeiro', *Deutsches Atlantikwall Archiv* No. 34 (Verlag Harry Lipman, Köln, 1999)

Enquist, O, *Kuivasaari* (Gummerus Kirjapaino Oy, Jyväskylä, 1995)

Eschenbacher, J, Ritter von, *Über moderne Artillerie* (Bernhard Friedrich Voigt Verlag, Weimar, 1872)

Fjeld, T, *et al*, *Klar til Strid. Kystartilleriet gjennom århundrene. Kystartilleriet Offiserforening.* (Nikolai olsens Trykkeri a.s., Kolbotn, 1999)

—————, *Der 28-cm Drillingsturm von Lundahauge, Ørland* (Ørland Kommune, 1994)

Förster, Th, 'Das Mukranwrack – Ein ungewöhnlicher Schiffsfund aus dem 16 Jahrhundert', *Nachrichtenblatt Arbeitskreis Unterwasserarchäologie*, 5-99

Fransson, Stig A, *Bofors 350 sr. Bofors AB* (Probus Förlag HB, Stockholm, 1996)

Frantzen, O L, *et al*, *Dansk Søartilleri 1400-2000* (Tøjhusmuseet Kopenhagen, 1999)

Galster, C, *Die Schiffs- und Küstengeschütze der deutschen Marine* (Siegfried Mittler und Sohn, Berlin, 1885, reprinted Walter F E Andraeas Verlag, Hamburg, 1993)

Gröner, E, *Die deutschen Kriegsschiffe 1815-1936* (J F Lehmanns Verlag, München, 1937)

Harnier, W von, 'Artillerie im Küstenkampf', *Wehrwissenschaftliche Berichte* Vol 7 (J F Lehmanns Verlag, München)

Howard, F, *Segel-Kriegssciffe 1400-1860* (Bernhard & Graefe Verlag, Koblenz, 1989)

Hughes, Q, and Migos, K, *Strong as the Rock of Gibraltar* (Exchange Publications, Gibraltar, 1995)

Jensen, O L, *The Royal Danish Naval Museum* (RDNM, Copenhagen, 1994)

Kosar, F, *Eisenbahngeschütze der Welt* (Motorbuch Verlag, Stuttgart, 1999)

Lanitzki, G, *Die WASA von 1628* (Transpress Verlag, Berlin, 1984)

—————, *Versunken in Ostsee – Schiffe und Schätze auf dem Meeresgrund* (Koehlers Verlagsgesellschaft mbH, Hertford, 1993)

Lewis, E R, *Seacoast Fortifications of the United States* (Pictorial Histories Publishing Company, Missoula, 1979)

Martini, J A, *Fort Point* (Golden Gate National Park Association, 1991)

Marine-Artillerie fremder Staten. Anhang zum Artillerie-Unterrichte für die K K Kriegsmarine (Jg von Kleinmayer printers, Bamberg, 1882)

Mondfeld, zu, W, *Schiffsgeschütze 1350 bis 1870* (Koehlers Verlagsgesellschaft mbH, Herford, 1988), Vol 1

Padfield, P, *Waffen auf See* (Verlag Delius Klasing & Co, Bielefeld u. Berlin, 1973)

Palao, G, *The Guns and Towers of Gibraltar* (Gibralta Bookshop, 1975)

Pataj, S, *Artyleria Ladowa 1871-1970* (Wydawnictwo Ministerstwa Obrony Narodowej, Warsaw, 1975)

Potter, E B, *Illustrated History of the United States Navy* (US Naval Academy, T Y Crowell Co, 1971)

Prasky, F, *Die Tegetthof-Klasse. Modellbau-Technik-Geschichte* (Verlag Österreich, Wien und Mittler & Sohn Hamburg, 2000)

Roth, R, *Field List. Zusammenstellung historischer und technischer Daten von untersuchten und vermessen Geschützen von 1420 bis 1870* (extract)

—————, *The Visser Collection. Arms of the Netherlands in the Collection of H L Visser* (Waanders Publishers, Zwolle, 1996), Vol II

Sarty, R F, *Coast Artillery 1815-1914* (Museum Restoration Service, Bloomfield, Ont., 1988)

Schmalenbach, P, *Die Geschichte der deutschen Schiffsartillerie* (Koehlers Verlagsgesellschaft mbH, Herford, 1993)

Schmeelke, M, *Alarm Küste. Deutsche Marine-, Heeres- und Luftwaffenbatterien in der Küstenverteidigung 1939-1945* (Pozdun-Pallas-Verlag, Wölfsheim, 1996)

Shirokorad, A B, 'Korabelnaja artillerija Rossiskogo Flota 1867-1922', *Morskaja Kollekzija* No 2/97 (1997)

Steensen, R S, *Fregatten Jylland* (Nationalmuseet, Selskrabet Fregatten Jylland. Andelsbogtrykkeriet Odense, 1965)

Terzibaschitsch, S, *Kreuzer der US Navy* (Koehlers Verlagsgesellschaft mbH, Herford, 1984)

—————, *Zerstörer der US Navy* (Koehlers Verlagsgesellschaft mbH, Herford, 1986)

Unterrichtsstafeln für Geschützkunde. Bd. 1, Seeziel. (Zusammengestellt bei der 1. Abteilung Schiffsartillerieschule, 1942)

Werkschronik, *50 Jahre Rheinmetall Düsseldorf 1889-1939* (A Bagel, Düsseldorf, 1939)

Werner, D u I, 'Maksim Gorki II: A Recent Example of the Re-use of Naval Turrets in Coast Defences', *Warship International* 1/1997

Wittwer, C, *Deutsche Schiffsartillerie an Land*, Marine-Arsenal Special Band 7 (Pozdun-Pallas-Verlag, Wölfsheim, 1997)

Index

Abbreviations

AH = Austria-Hungary; Aus = Australia;
BL = breech-loader; Bul = Bulgaria;
Brz = Brazil; Can = Canada; Den = Denmark;
DP = dual-purpose; Fin = Finland;
Fr = France; Ger = Germany; Gib = Gibraltar;
Gr = Greece; HMAS = His Majesty's
Australian Ship; HMSM = His Majesty's
Submarine; It = Italy; Jpn = Japan;
MC = machine cannon; MG = machine gun;
ML = muzzle-loader; Neth = Netherlands;
Nor = Norway; Phil = Phillipines; Pol = Poland;
RML = rifled muzzle-loader; Rus = Russia/
Soviet Union; Sing = Singapore; Sp = Spain;
Swe = Sweden; TBG = torpedo boat gun;
Tur = Turkey

Index of Ships, Forts and Museums

Cast iron culverin, cast by I. Phillips in England for Portugal in 1587.

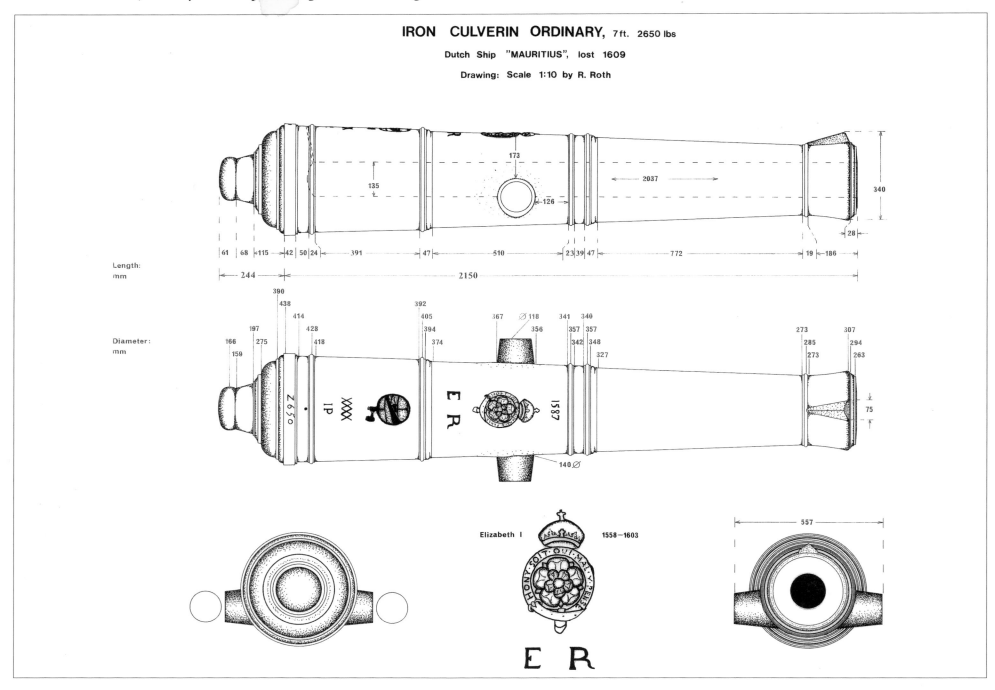

IRON CULVERIN ORDINARY, 7 ft. 2650 lbs

Dutch Ship "MAURITIUS", lost 1609

Drawing: Scale 1:10 by R. Roth

Length:
mm

Diameter:
mm

Elizabeth I   1558—1603

E R